Adventuring WITH *Beebe*

Selections from the writings of

WILLIAM BEEBE

DIRECTOR EMERITUS
DEPARTMENT OF TROPICAL RESEARCH
NEW YORK ZOOLOGICAL SOCIETY

With Illustrations

The Viking Press · *New York*

EXPLORER BOOKS EDITION
ISSUED IN 1960 BY THE VIKING PRESS, INC.
625 MADISON AVENUE, NEW YORK 22, N.Y.

DISTRIBUTED IN CANADA BY
THE MACMILLAN COMPANY OF CANADA LIMITED

The material from *Nonsuch: Land of Water* (1932), *Zaca Venture* (1938), and *Book of Bays* (1942) is reprinted with the permission of Harcourt, Brace & Co., Inc.

This edition published by arrangement with
Duell, Sloan & Pearce, Inc.

PRINTED IN THE U.S.A. BY THE COLONIAL PRESS INC.

Author's Note

These tales cover more than forty years of time; they range from Bermuda to British Guiana and the Pearl Islands, from the tops of lofty jungle trees to a half mile beneath the sea.

They deal with varied wildlife from black inchling fish which live in the eternal darkness of ocean's abyss to thirty-five-foot whale sharks in full sun at the surface.

They tell of birds from the all but flightless hoatzin to wandering albatrosses with wingspread of eleven feet. We shall become acquainted with all sorts of creatures; but whether butterfly, dolphin, lizard or snail, all are our neighbors through life and time on this good earth of ours, and hence traveling companions, whose lives it is a joy to watch and a privilege to share.

WILLIAM BEEBE

Simla, Arima Valley
Trinidad, B.W.I.

Contents

I BERMUDA STATION

1 Mount Bermuda   3

2 Almost Island   14

3 Feathered Tourists   32

4 Cahows and Longtails   42
    (from *Nonsuch: Land of Water*)

5 A First Round Trip to Davy Jones's Locker   54

6 Contour Diving   85
    (from *Half Mile Down*)

II PACIFIC CRUISE

7 Albatrosses   93

8 Flight Patterns   103

9 Whale-Sharking   109

10 Clarion: The Lonely Isle   116
    (from *Zaca Venture*)

11 Going Ashore   129

12 River of Mud   140

13 A Touch of Purgatory   151

14 Salvador — De Omnibus Rebus   160

15 Papagayo Paradise   176

16 Pacific Jungle   190
    (from *Book of Bays*)

III JUNGLE LIFE

17 Hoatzins at Home   205

18 A Yard of Jungle   215
    (from *Jungle Peace*)

19 A Bit of Uselessness   230

20 The Bay of Butterflies   237
       (from *Edge of the Jungle*)

21 St. Francis of the Plaster Cast   251
       (from *High Jungle*)

Illustrations

Flight rhythm of pelicans and cormorants *page* 107

HALFTONES *following* page 138
Bermuda shoreline
Bird blind on Nonsuch
Nestling cahow
Parent cahow
Giant binoculars
Our greatest danger
Whale shark
Marooned with a boa constrictor
Nestling hoatzin climbing
Head of adult hoatzin
Hummingbird drinking from heliconia
Binoculars and plaster cast
Tree fern in the cloud forest; shaking insects into an umbrella
Painting air plants on the jungle floor
Collecting nocturnal Jungle creatures

I

Bermuda Station

CHAPTER 1

Mount Bermuda

IT was half past four in the afternoon of the Second Day of Creation, and in a drowned world I was wet and cold and hungry and idle and bored. Then things began to happen inside my mind, and at four forty-five I was still wet, but neither cold nor hungry nor idle, and hence not bored.

At the very tip of the long, southward-pointing finger of Nonsuch is a small cliff jutting out to sea between two little gorges, and on the uttermost point I was perched in a deluge of rain, hugging my knees and wishing for the sun. Only the day before I had been desirous of knowing something of the beginning of Nonsuch and of Bermuda, and now, suddenly, I realized that my wish had been answered, and instead of squatting, disgruntled and bored, I focused all my imagination on making the most of this cosmic opportunity. There must have been a moon in existence somewhere in the firmament beyond all this dampness, for the tide was high, although the horizontal water was quite hidden by the vertical downpour.

The isolation of my perch was such that not a particle of land — dry or otherwise — was visible. I would not have been surprised if a school of active fish had dashed past, and twice I glanced obliquely upward, half expecting to see the keel of a boat as when I am submerged in the diving helmet. I could breathe only by keeping my head well down. Every portion of my body was wet, so having nothing for comparison, I was not conscious of moisture. At first I had been aware of dripping and splashing and the slap of waves, but these, by interminable repetition, had become part of underwater silence.

I might have been the last of the evil pre-Noahites, about to slip into oblivion. And then even this conceit left me, and I attained a damp Nirvana; hunger, cold, wetness, boredom were forgotten, and I was an utterly inadequate but appreciative mind looking on at the birth of Bermuda.

Students of the planets and of our jolly, round, whirling earth have given us an estimate of cosmic evolution considerably longer that that of the Bible. I have known days, indeed, which seemed like eternity, and Einstein tells us that space annihilates both ether and time. Still, the human mind likes to mumble definite figures, even though they are far beyond actual appreciation. So I recalled with moist satisfaction that the birth of the seven seas must have been somewhere around a billion years ago. This seemed ancient even to me on my oceanic pedestal, and my mind flew ahead to the time, many millions of years ago, when the volcanos of the western Atlantic began to push and boil upward. Unlike the usual cluster of such outbursts, that of Bermuda was solitary in mid-ocean. In the West Indies and Antilles, seven or eight hundred miles to the south, there were scores of neighborly outlets which nosed their way up from the bottom into light and air, and far across the Atlantic, twenty-five hundred miles east, the volcanic constellation of the Azores broke surface.

Here in complete isolation, at the bidding of some deep-hidden geological factor, the lava began to ooze forth, and after an inconceivable chemical battle with the icy waters two miles down piled up the scarlet, molten rock from the very vitals of Mother Earth, pitting its three thousand degrees of sheer heat against the all but freezing point of the water, backed by two tons of pressure to the inch. As far as we know today, this mountain reached the surface with one peak, to a southernmost particle of which I was now clinging. But on the slopes of this great submarine massif two mighty cones stretched themselves up — so high that they made of Bermuda almost a trio of island centers. Today they are known as the Challenger and Argus banks, flat-topped peaks, fifteen and thirty miles off shore and only a few fathoms beneath the surface. I have dredged the former from the *Arcturus* and gleaned a great mass of seaweed and reef animals, and I have fished it from the *Gladisfen* and found it aboil with sharks. This is Bermuda Mountain as we know it today.

But, to go back, here was I blinded and surrounded by water, and all I knew of the world was that I rested on a hard bit of crag — so Bermuda must be above water. The Third Day of Genesis was yet to dawn, for early therein is a mention of dry land and that was, to my senses, yet to come. Shifting my cramped limbs, I slipped and slid down the rivulets and waterfalls until by the mere cessation of liquid sound I knew I had reached the level of most of our globe. The downpour had long ago flattened whatever motion the ocean might have had of its own. I dipped still farther — the rain ceased to pelt my knees and shoulders, and I knew I was neck deep under the sea. I reached out and swashed the water back and forth, and something stuck between my fingers. I plucked at it and palmed it and climbed back upon the only material in the world which was not water. Bracing my toes into convenient crevices, I shook the water from my eyes and gazed mistily at what I had salvaged from the waves. Vague messages traveled from eyes to mind — strangely, from a forgotten world, a world which held such qualities as sunlight and dryness, an unwatery world. I held a grape in my hand — that idea persisted for a long time — and I looked steadily at it between drops, trying to picture the necessary dryness which was required to make of a grape a reality. I had almost succeeded when a spark of accessory memory made it plain that this could not be a grape. It might have been several other things, but its actualness burst upon me, and for a few minutes I experienced the joy which has come only twice before in my life, when I have been playing a silly game with myself and my mind (as at present, hugging the idea of the Second Day of Creation) and suddenly have had Earth or Sky or Cosmos take a hand, lean down, and play with me. I felt like Ord when he glimpsed the hand of the Player, enormous in the sky, over the heads of the gods. Only in my case it was nothing but a little green sphere, which, if very hard, might have been an emerald; if sheltering a cluster of small seeds, would most assuredly have been a grape. My second memory was correct, and I knew my fingers had closed upon a *Halicystis* floating in this waste of waters. And the knowledge that it was this made me shout aloud into the world of drops that the Third Day of Creation had dawned, and I was here to see! But if I am to be a consistent surveyor of the evolution of Nonsuch, I must keep my *Halicystis* shut away for a while in my closed fist and pretend I have not yet seen it.

Bermuda has two nicknames which to us on Nonsuch are gross misnomers. One is "The Isles of Rest." This slogan comes stamped across our envelopes and for the average tourist is doubtless very true. To us, whose workday is measured only by our physical being's absolute limit of energy, it is only comic. The second is "Coral Islands," when as a matter of fact there is not a particle of coral in the inorganic make-up of Bermuda. Living coral, in small and large heads, is indeed abundant on the submerged reefs, although even here it is only a veneer of encrusted life.

Bermuda is undoubtedly the apex of a mighty volcanic mountain. A recent deep boring, made in the hope of finding fresh water, failed completely in its purpose but provided absolute proof of ancient volcanic activity. The first three hundred and sixty feet showed limestone such as we find today everywhere in Bermuda. For the next two hundred feet yellowish claylike rocks represented decomposed volcanic tufa. From here down to the extreme limit of boring, fourteen hundred feet, there was nothing but black volcanic rock, and this undoubtedly extended down to the very ocean floor. The only lava I have seen is a bit from the gizzard of a sandpiper freshly arrived from Greenland. Everywhere, on all the islands, are crags and cliffs and outcroppings of stratified rock, soft where newly exposed and hardened to the consistency of marble where lashed by breakers. The multitude of superimposed leaves of stone do not mark past lava flows or deposits on an ancient sea bottom, but sheets of wind-blown sand swirled over prehistoric dunes.

As long as my watery world reigned supreme, I could well mark my data as millions upon millions of years B.C., but when the low afternoon sun began to sift through the rain, and I could dimly see the fissures and crags of the hardened wind-blown rocks of Nonsuch, then eons of time passed quickly, and I again came down the scale to, geologically speaking, almost contemporary times — say in early Pleistocene, about a million years back.

Here we have a geological conundrum: At this time, ten thousand centuries ago, let us suppose we have a potential Bermuda submerged a little distance beneath the surface of the ocean. How can we make this into isles of rest without raising the crest of the submerged volcano or adding coral or other material to its summit?

The only logical remaining possibility appears to be absurd — the lowering of the ocean itself — and yet this is exactly what happened. If a pail of water is allowed partly to freeze overnight and the ice then removed, the level of the remaining water will be considerably lowered. So, many years ago in the Pleistocene, great windstorms carried away vast quantities of water, drawn up into clouds from the oceans, and deposited it as snow over all the northern lands of the world. The snow then turned into ice and pushed southward, and the first glacial epoch began. Little by little, as more water piled up on the land, the level of the Atlantic Ocean sank, and Bermuda Mountain came nearer and nearer to the surface. Finally, when over a half-mile thickness of ice had formed, the level of the sea was lowered over two hundred and fifty feet, leaving Bermuda high and dry.

Dry Bermuda at this time was of considerable extent, and the terrific windstorms probably prevented the growth of any vegetation. But snails — uncounted hosts of snails — barnacles, sea urchins, bryozoans, and other shelly creatures found the shores excellent for existence and thrived. Generations died and their homes were smashed by the waves and ground up into sand, and this was blown into high dunes and cemented by the rain. "And so, Best Beloved," was written the second chapter of Bermuda. When I stand upon the summit of Nonsuch and look eastward toward Coopers, or south to Gurnets or west to Castle, I see everywhere the paper-thin records of past wind-borne sand (more euphoniously, aeolian), once fine as powder, now hardened into limestone or very marble. And when I dive four or five fathoms down to the bottom of Nonsuch Bay, or farther out, at Almost Island, on the edge of the ocean abyss itself, there again are everywhere the fixed records of ancient dunes.

The first time I drove across Bermuda I noticed in the sheer limestone walls where the road cut deep into the hills an occasional stratum of rich red loam, many feet beneath the present surfaces. It remained for Dr. Sayles, when on a visit to me on Nonsuch, to make plain the meaning of the several layers of earth lying between the numerous records of ancient wind-blown sand. They represent the successive interglacial periods of warmth, when the water would rise, reducing the exposed surface and curtailing the wind-blown dunes whose formation necessitated considerable areas above water. During periods such as these, the conditions would be much like the present, when the cessation of constant movement of shifting sand would permit the establishment and growth of plant life and the slow accumulation of earth and mold. In the course of time there would come another glacial period, with a re-exposing of great extents of surface, and the whirling sands would quickly destroy and bury the plants and the collected soil. And so on, until it seems certain that we can recognize no fewer than four distinct soils, representing as many interglacial times of windless warmth.

As the rain slackened and the afternoon sun grew stronger, I saw, from my semiaquatic seat, the gray and black crags about me. Beneath my hand was a thickened slab with six delicate layers, the fourth twice the depth of the others. I fingered this particular layer, crumbled its edge into sand grains, and flung a handful into the air. And then I tried to imagine the mighty wind which had last swirled these over the dunes and into that other air — hot or cold — which blew over this spot at least fifty thousand years before the first glimmerings of historic human life. And I and my work and my opinions seemed, like Kim, to be very small and of very little account and of no real importance whatever. I began to muse on what was the use of it all and why bother about anything any longer, and because this, like some charity, is only an inverted form of egotism and conceit, my partner in my silly game of long ago sprang another surprise. I noticed that there was a mist of sorts between me and the stratified sand nearby. I looked up and as far as emotional effect went, a full charge of HE might have gone off at my elbow. I experienced a visual shell shock, for high overhead there was etched the strongest, most materialistic rainbow I have ever seen — one end began in mid-air, and the other curved down, down, down, holding true from red to violet, to the rocks beside me. Once before, on a Guiana jungle river, I had been actually at the end of a rainbow, when, at my very side, one colored the bulwarks of our Akawai dugout.

As I stood up, I dropped my *Halicystis* grape, but swiftly salvaged it again as it bobbed about on the water, not because of its rarity, but by reason of its part in my game. For on the Third Day of Creation, some hundreds of millions of years ago, when the waters and the sky and the earth had been running satisfactorily for a while, there appeared the first living organisms comparable to my pseudogrape. For several reasons the round green *Halicystis* was the most appropriate of modern living beings to play the part of one of the earliest of organisms. First of all, it is a plant, an alga, and plants certainly preceded animals. And secondly, it is a single cell, and unquestionably the *Protophyta* are the most accurately named of all groups. Again, many creatures of ancient times amaze us with their astounding size — pterodactyls, dragonflies, brontosaurs, titanotheres, moas — all exceeding any corresponding organisms living on the earth today. In *Halicystis* we have a contemporary miracle, no less wonderful than would be a living six-foot ant, or a fifty-foot dog, or a hundred-foot man. When we think of a single cell, we think automatically of something microscopic, such as the cells in the human body which have a maximum diameter of a fraction of a millimeter. In *Halicystis*, however, we have a large green marble, probably the largest cell in the world.

Aside from its interest, so germane to my present mood, *Halicystis* is a very remarkable organism. The Bermudians call them sea bottles, and after storms they are sometimes found in dozens washed ashore along the south beach on Nonsuch. They have great resiliency and when fresh and alive will bounce five or six feet from a smooth surface. When the sun shines brightly upon a group on the sand just as they have been left by the waves, their beauty is that of polished emeralds — the sunlight passing through their translucent green substance and deeply staining their thin shadow.

They may be round or pyriform, and no one knows where they begin life, whether hidden beneath some rock near shore or, as is more probable, farther out in the mysterious mid-zone. Unlike related forms, when freed from their slight attachment, they float buoyantly. In an aquarium they will live for a week or more and then gradually pale out until they are like ghosts of grapes and, little by little, settle to the bottom with only a few jade-colored granules in place of the nucleus and all the complex vital mechanism of this "simple" plant of the sea. I have measured a *Halicystis* one and one half inches in diameter, and they have been reported to grow as large as a hen's egg. The ease of collection of this and related sea bottles and the extraordinary size of these single cells have led to the detailed study of the effects of electricity and various chemical compounds and elements upon them — experimentation which may conceivably lead to better knowledge of cellular health and disease in the human body.

In the course of my more serious researches, to which these essays may be said to be only an authentic fringe, I made a series of dredge hauls on the bottom of my deep-sea study area. One memorable day my sturdy little cobweb of wire brought the big dredge to the surface twelve miles off shore. Soundings had shown that the bottom here was fifteen hundred fathoms, or a full mile and a half beneath our keel. The dredge frame was twisted and bent into a V by the roughness over which it had passed, which was in itself surprising, for at such a depth the bottom of the ocean, even if rolling, is usually smooth.

The netting itself was not torn, and although there were only a few handfuls of abyssal loot at the end, these were most unexpected. They consisted wholly of water-worn shells, bits of coral, and rounded pebbles — indisputable proofs of a submerged beach. There were half a hundred of one species of white bivalve which has been found fossil in Bermuda cliffs thirty feet above the present ocean level, and most of the shells were of West Indian species.

So here is an entirely new glimpse of the past of Bermuda. The glacial earths and wind-blown sand are unquestionably facts. But ages and ages before the terrestrial tides of ice ebbed and flowed, the bottom of the sea hereabouts would seem, by some unprecedented extent of upheaval, to have been dry land.

At present Bermuda has nearly the same area as Manhattan Island — about twenty square miles; when the ocean was partly evaporated into ice, it multiplied this nearly twelve times, while a conservative estimate of dry land, if my mile-and-a-half-deep beaches cannot be otherwise explained, would give to Bermuda an area of almost six hundred square miles.

There seems no possible chance of the shells and pebbles having rolled or fallen to these great depths down such a gentle slope, and the fact of their being the same as those from the West Indies gives the whole matter great significance.

In spite of all these new and exciting discoveries, I still get sheer joy out of my first game. And today when I walk on Nonsuch Beach, with the storm's aftermath pounding on the sand, not only do the small, stranded green globes appeal to me with their intrinsic beauty, but they recall the delight that one of them gave when it so fittingly ushered into my imagination the dawn of the Third Day of Creation — a matter of more than half a billion years gone by.

CHAPTER 2

Almost Island

SIX years ago I drifted in the *Arcturus* for ten days in the Pacific, hovering above a certain spot in mid-ocean and by dredge, net, and sounding wire learning everything I could about this invisible but very real bit of submerged earth.

Six days ago I made my first map of Almost Island, south of Nonsuch, and northeast of Gurnets Rock. We are accustomed to speak of air pockets and mountain chains and hanging valleys, so why cannot we have something which is almost an island? The distinction is much more accurate than that between hill and mountain, creek and river. I might, in fact, call my area Once Island, for from its configuration and our knowledge of the land hereabouts, there is no doubt that it was formerly well above water.

I discovered it by accident three years ago when I rowed out to Gurnets, threw out the anchor at random, and went down in the helmet. I found myself in five or six fathoms on the whitest of sand, looking up at the walls of a splendid reef — great cliffs waving with sea fans and alive with fish. The minute the helmet was removed, I located the spot definitely in its relation to Gurnets Rock — two hundred yards southwest of my boat and marked by a giant angle in the center of the reef.

Almost Island is in an exposed position, separated from the open sea by only a few yards of reefs and boilers. Swells coming in do not actually break, but they swirl around the boilers and begin to slow up and gain height at the friction of the shallows. My first problem was to arrange for a safe landing whenever the wind and sea permitted. We tried throwing out an anchor to windward, with the result that we usually lost the anchor or had a difficult time freeing it, and often the stern of the launch would swing in a quarter circle, chafing the metal ladder against the reef. A heavy piece of iron and a chain attached to a log buoy well to windward helped, and finally another far out on the sand made my island easy of access; the boat was like a double-moored zeppelin over an inaccessible island above water.

Proper islands are delineated by geographers and the makers of maps with rulers and compasses, squares and dividers. I was my own dividers in the present instance.

While my bit of land more than justified the name of island by being surrounded with water, yet its actual area was extremely personal and ungeographic. I estimate it to be roughly circular and about one hundred and fifty feet in diameter. As I say, I was the measuring dividers — the pump on the launch being the center, the hose the radial string, and I the pen or pencil or marker on the periphery.

My apparatus is, of course, our old story — the same double-action pump, a forty-foot metal ladder, two generous lengths of hose, and the metal helmet with four weights which I have used for years in the Galápagos and West Indies. The helmets are dull now and show hard usage, dents from overhanging Galápagos lava blocks, scratches from the low-arched tunnels of Cocos and Panama and the branching coral in Haiti. But they are as good as ever, fitting to the back and shoulder like well-worn clothing.

The helmet on, I straightened out and slid down the ladder, reaching out my hand now and then to orient myself. Two swallows en route are usually sufficient to equalize the air pressure in my ears. I touched bottom gently, settled my helmet, and looked up. This is probably the most instinctive movement of anyone, beginners or old veteran divers — a desire to make certain that the only line of retreat is open. Daily overhead I saw the amusing keel of the launch rolling slowly in the swell — the fore and aft ropes looping into blue distance — and the long sinuous black snake of a hose, with my head in its maw and its tail vanishing above the keel. The ladder waved slowly back and forth, from the sand beneath my feet up to heaven, and while I was not privileged to see angels ascending and descending, I did rejoice in the sight of jolly sergeant majors, or abudefdufs, as I prefer to call them, with black stripes over green and gold, weaving in and out in my wake. They had already scented the bit of high bait I was carrying and to them I was only the harmless conveyor of something exciting and edible. A last glance up showed two things — first, a rather nice submarine joke, for close on the tail of the last abudefduf hastened a young angelfish, and I chuckled and felt that Jacob in his vision had nothing on the realities of Almost Island; and second, I saw a square window opening into my other world — my assistant peering down through the waterglass. I waved and then the whole upper seascape was obliterated by a rush of my breath bubbles, and I turned to the affairs of the island.

My island is divided almost equally into sand and reef, and these correspond to all the varied phases of dry physical geography — sand taking the place of deserts, plains, pampas and tundras, and a reef embodying mountains, canyons and jungles.

We do not think of there being weather under water, but if we consider terrestrial weather as heat, cold, dryness, moisture, wind, rain, snow and fog, then my submerged islet has weather in abundance. I may descend in water which feels delightfully warm to my skin, but in half an hour I come shivering to the surface with teeth chattering; of dryness, we submariners know nothing, except concerning our face, and when dryness leaves the helmet, we expire or ascend; as for moisture, we have nothing else but.

Wind and fog are interesting; the latter on land is caused by minute particles of water, while beneath-the-surface fog is a result of small particles of land. I have visited my island when I could not see more than a yard away — the water was merely diluted sand. A distant gale had sent in great swells which reached down, down, and plowed the sand into deep transverse furrows, while the suspended grains flicked against the glass of my helmet like atoms made visible. To see the reef or a great fish loom up through this pale-blue fog is a sight to be forever remembered. In a heavy swell the water is often filled with fronds and strands of seaweed, torn off by the surge near the surface and now, like beautiful autumn leaves, eddying back and forth — bits of wine-colored lace, or long fronds shimmering in the diluted sunlight with exquisite opalescence.

Undersea wind is once removed from wind overhead, since it is the motion of water caused in turn by the motion of air. I never realized how absolutely still water could be until I looked out from my bathysphere into the blue quiet a quarter mile down. In that place there was no such thing actually as plankton, for no matter how slight a power of movement any creature might have, even if it shot about only in circles, yet the movement and direction were its own.

On my island in a heavy wind swell all of us, the fish and myself, became very nearly plankton, being pushed forward and withdrawn at the will of the water. Six fathoms down day and night are unlike those on land — the former being much shorter. My island is in full illumination from ten to three o'clock, preceded and followed by a prolonged dawn and dusk. It is as though the eternal night of all except the surface film of ocean was reluctant to admit any light. But my eyes become dusk-adapted very soon, and even in cloudy weather I can watch my tenants, little and big.

The reef cliffs are sandstone, etched and worn into arches, turrets, alleys, tunnels, wells, canyons and a thousand unnamable forms by the wind and rain of some past glacial age when all were high and dry. This is overlaid and frescoed with great balls of brain coral, and hung and planted with rainbow-tinted seaweed and purple and brown sea fans and plumes. In and out of the tangled scenery swim hosts of fish, great parti-colored parrots, surgeons of heavenly blue, angelfish, groupers, rockfish, snappers, agile wrasse of a hundred colors, and small folk by the dozen.

But this is not an ichthyological reconnaissance; it is a visit to Almost Island. Access made easy, what can I do? First and last in importance in our work is concentrated observation — remembered facts of color, movement, feeding, sociability, courtship, abundance — but I wish also to collect any new species I see, or any which defy identification on the fin.

First comes the small trident with a three-foot metal handle. This requires the most careful stalking and yields poorest results, yet I have again and again caught a desired fish close to the reef wall on the sand, and by a very sudden and forceful thrust have impaled my game. I have now, however, relegated Neptune's weapon, together with air rifles, to the island armory of relics. The most efficient arm is a wire arrow projected through a short bit of pipe by means of a large rubber band — a cross between a slingshot and a bow and arrow.

My last foray will serve as a type of submarine collecting. I dropped to the bottom with my arrow sling in my hand and leaning down, picked up the trident. There was only a gentle surge, what we might call a water breeze, and I leaned against it and pushed south to my favorite angle. With one hand I lifted myself three feet, found a hollow for my foot, and looked around. A short distance ahead was a huge spined urchin, hundreds of its twelve-inch black needles forming an impenetrable chevaux-de-frise. With the trident I jabbed lustily into this mass, threw the instrument behind me on the sand, and stepped down again.

Now I performed an acrobatic feat which would win fame and fortune in vaudeville. I waited until the surge was half through the backward push and leaped upward with all my might. Slowly I rose and rose off the sand, higher and higher, being carried all the time slightly back and away from the reef. At my greatest elevation the surge shifted, hung on dead center a moment, and then carried me forward and over the edge of the wall of coral and sea plumes. My gentle descent had already begun so that at the end of the trajectory I found myself close to the place from which I had chosen to operate. Keeping an upright balance was the only thing to be careful about en route, but at the minute of landing it was necessary to dig in at once. With all my fingers, and my feet in their mobile, rubber-soled sneakers, I grasped every projection possible. In this case I found I could even jam an angle of the helmet against an overhanging corner. All this was to prevent my being swept off the reef by the retreating surge and to guard against scraping in the opposite direction on razor-sharp corals and still more unpleasant spiny urchins. The one I had stabbed was close by, and the stream of luscious odor-taste pouring forth had already proved a magnet to a school of sergeant majors. Fish are like vultures and when they see an excited mob of abudefdufs milling around a certain spot, no hint of odor or taste is needed to urge them to hurry to the place. The sequence is much the same as a light in the water at night, or a great jungle tree felled in the tropics — first come the smaller creatures, then the larger, and finally the great carnivores, who are attracted not by the lure of bait, or light, or bark, but by the chance of feeding on the mob itself.

I sat with rubber sling drawn taut, feet braced against the surge, but body and head giving as much as possible to it. Here is a real undersea rhythm, not found anywhere else, to which every fish and floating form of life, every loose strand of weed or plume, all with one impulse swing slowly first in one direction, then all back again. I aimed at fish after fish, and then an unusually colored rock-fish drifted out from between my legs and I let go. He was larger and stronger than I thought, and with a half dozen tremendous flicks he tore loose. Instead of fleeing, he turned and snapped at the arrow point, which still held several scales.

Smaller fish were easy to hold when once the arrow was well through, and the astonishing thing was that after being shaken off into a pail, they recovered and later in an aquarium swam upright and healed quickly. When an arrow merely grazed the side of a fish, it invariably turned and bit at the weapon and then swam off and rubbed its scaleless patch against coral and reef. A badly wounded fish which escaped illustrated one of the fundamental laws of this underworld — one which holds in all the places and oceans where I have dived. An uninjured fish is comparatively safe, but an injured one is attacked and killed by every carnivorous fish in sight, including the members of its own school. Even the parrots and the surgeons mill excitedly about and seem to deplore the fact that they are vegetarians and can take no part in this summary execution. To us it seems cruel, or a better term, perhaps, is inhuman, in the real meaning of the word. If our far distant ancestors had not kept the race fit in some such way, perhaps we would not today have the stamina to carry on and yet cherish our weaklings and cripples, wage war with poison gas instead of clubs, and too often forget the joy of hard creative work.

The most successful method of individual collecting on Almost Island is with a fish pole and a dynamite cap at the end. "Fisherman's luck" is a truism where traps, nets and angling are concerned, but this underwater shooting which we have invented elevates the collecting of fish into the realm of true sport.

On one of my last descents I located two schools of young fish. I had a hand net, but I might as well have tried to capture a pheasant on the wing with a butterfly net. The net swung so slowly through this dense medium that the youngsters did not even hurry; they simply slipped to one side into safety.

I ascended swiftly, asked for the dynamite cap, and descended. Sand once more underfoot I saw the fish pole standing upright beside me. With the net in my belt, the pole in my right hand, the insulated electric wire in the other, I was ready for action. I drifted slowly toward the smaller school of iridescent fish, stretched out my pole into their midst as far as I could, turned my head, and pulled thrice on a small rubber cable. Instantly my ears were deafened and my body and limbs tingled as from a wholesale electric shock. I invariably felt of the edges of the glass after an explosion to see if all was right. Formerly I used to rest the apparatus on a bit of projecting reef and placing some bait near the cap, fire it from a distance. Now I do not mind holding the end of the five-foot pole, but as yet I have not been able to summon sufficient courage to face the explosion.

I dropped the pole and it was drawn swiftly up; then I began to weave the net back and forth in the water, scooping in the floating silvery motes. I dared not stop the movement or the net would turn inside out. I found small fish of other species drifting in a little distance away, but I had to work fast, for the fish were usually only stunned and soon began to recover. In such fashion I gathered fifty-odd, and on deck we found they were beautiful little pear-shaped infants, all shining gold and silver with enormous gleaming eyes, blessed with the title of *Pempheris*, but no popular name.

A more exciting use of the dynamite cap was in shooting larger fish, and this hunting demanded every bit of my skill — the search for and the discovery of some desired species, the cunning stalk over sand and reef, both hunter and game at the mercy of the swell, and finally the advance of the little red lozenge, the signal, the invariable flinching, and the instant pursuit and capture of the upturned fish to forestall any of its fellows, who would at once rush in to the attack. With this sport and that of shooting flying fish from the bow of a launch no game-bird hunter away from his coverts or preserves or jungles need be bored.

At first sight the sand appeared barren as a desert, but I spent many dives sitting or lying as flat as my helmet would permit, watching the tenants of the shifting grains. At certain angles and strength of current and tide the very furrows seem to be alive — having movement and rhythm — and I am sure if I had a microphone I could hear the sand grains singing together.

I once sat far out on the flat white expanse when the water was quite clear. I could feel the very slight push and slack of the swell, but the surface of the sand was troubled with a wholly different force. When my whole being was impelled forward, the crests of the furrows beyond me loosened, thousands of glittering motes rose a little, then tumbled down the slope and up the flank of the succeeding furrow. I stopped calling them furrows and recognized them as new and strange waves, tuned, like my own actions, into slow-motion imitations of our corresponding activities in another world. I saw that the sand waves were not stationary but were very slowly advancing. In five minutes my foot was well covered, and I visualized slow entombment if I stayed long enough — the creeping up and burying by the white arenaceous coverlet — and I knew how fossils must have felt in the making.

It is not easy to see and study the creatures of the sand from a six-foot distance. One must kneel or sit. Again and again a sliver of sand slips from beneath my hand, and a sand goby has shifted its position; or as I walk along, an active snowshoe dodges my step, and a great flounder undulates to safety. The thought of gobies gives me a conceit of sorts, for here in six fathoms I found sand gobies and reef gobies but never tide-pool gobies, and I realized that I — a mere land-bound human — had descended well below the realm of these shore fish. I once went to the trouble of carrying down a shore goby in a vial. After considerable difficulty with the cork, due to the increased pressure at this depth, I liberated him, and my ego was pleased to see him streak for the surface. I felt more at home than before, and hailed the sand gobies and blue surgeons and emerald parrots as brethren of the same cast as I — we who could make our way far below where *Bathygobius soporator* was comfortable. Such is submarine snobbishness!

Lizard fish and other sand-colored friends lived about me on the ocean floor, but as I sat quietly, unexpected visitors sometimes passed, paying no attention to this harmless projection seated in mid-sand, periodically spouting a geyser of bubbles. Without warning, two fish came toward me, side by side, each well over three feet in length, graceful and of superb beauty. They were yellowtails — oxidized silver, with a broad golden band along the sides. A yellowtail twelve inches in length is a large yellowtail to the Bermudian angler. These giants had small highbred heads and arched backs; toward the tail their bodies narrowed like an athlete's waist; and behind all there waved a mighty reversed crescent of a tail. Their movements were effortless, their path in life was assured, their desires distinctly attainable — they knew their stuff. For several yards they swam evenly, unhurriedly, then, one after the other, like perfectly synchronized parts of a single bit of mechanism, they dipped to the sand, each scooped up a great mouthful, and on the rise, sent it out in a flurry like dense smoke. Again and again they dipped and puffed, dipped and puffed, until in their wake there was a score of fading gouts of sand — like the vanishing sky blossoms of shrapnel smoke.

These and many others were passing visitors to my island, not to be watched for, because their size was unimaginable, their occupation unforeseen, their very presence wholly unexpected. Others were such permanent residents that I have named localities for them, such as Lobster Alley and Chub Canyon. Our pet lobster is of unusual size, and her antennae are forever protruding from the window of her apartment well up on a reef wall within a side canyon. Now and then I tweak her horns as I pass and she withdraws in insulted haste.

In Chub Canyon six or eight enormous chubs are always to be found. I do not think that a chub four feet over all has been captured in these islands, but here they are — records which would make an angler wild with envy.

With the water clear and free from sand and no fish as far as the eye could see, I once stopped at the foot of the ladder to pick up a net. As I straightened up, I got the most terrific shock I can remember underseas, for at first glance I seemed to be completely enclosed by some creature of enormous size. Within a second my eye had resolved the mass into hundreds upon hundreds of chubs, all about a foot in length, which had materialized in mid-water from nothing, and now swam so close that they shut out reef and sand, many of them almost within arm's reach — milling around and around me, apparently absorbed in interest in this being new to their cosmos. After several minutes another idea imbued the thousands, and as one fish, they turned and swam unhurriedly out and around the end of the reef. Five minutes passed before I began my ascent; the experience was too wonderful, the memory too vivid to be immediately disturbed.

I am amused to find that I have described the inhabitants of my island as living on sand or reef, and omitted the water itself, where the vast majority spend their lifetime. At certain seasons creatures appear who have nothing whatever to do with coral, reef, or sand. In September, when flocks of shore birds migrate to the beaches of Nonsuch, schools or, more properly, sheer hosts of individual creatures far different swim into my ken — the passing, day after day, of great sun jellies. They are so evanescent when viewed from below that I often detect them first by their shadows pulsating unevenly over the sand furrows — shadows which seem to possess more substance than their makers. When I am making my way with my arrows across a wide stretch of sand, I sometimes leap up eight or ten feet and impale one of these great living plaques, thrusting my lance through and through the creature, a submarine pigsticking of sorts. It is a tribute to the simplicity of the nervous system of jellies that they appear to be quite unaware that anything untoward has happened to their machinery, and vibrate calmly on, after the manner of all healthy jellyfish.

A fine white strand drifts across the glass of my helmet and I reach out and brush it casually aside. But it is no derelict bit of seaweed, for at my touch it curls and twists and withdraws upward. I sight along its slanting length, and high overhead, just dimly visible, at least thirty feet away near the surface, is a great *Cyanea* jelly, a half-bushel mass of deep lavender. As I look, it gently sinks and comes nearer, and I see the medusa head of a myriad tendrils. I side-step to avoid them, for they sting severely, and with the sun behind me I detect a crowd of little fish scurrying in and out of the deadly portieres. At that moment a black net filled with air bubbles appears and the jelly vanishes — my assistant has captured it, and we find that its attendant fish are little bumpers, quite new to Bermuda. Thousands of them spend their early life in these gorgon heads, generations having drifted for centuries past the Somers Isles without a single individual being cast ashore.

The first thing which questioners wish to know, and the last which occupies our minds, is the Dangers of Almost Island. Barracudas nose about us now and then, sharks but rarely in the daytime; morays of moderate length come to our bait, and green chaps of embarrassing circumference and extent have their homes in the deeper wells, but only occasionally do we see their gasping jaws; groupers, as in Haiti, are sometimes a trifle too curious and fearless. So far, however, I have been attacked only by inchling demoiselles, when I have perched too near their chosen domicile, although sergeant majors now and then harmlessly nip at ankle or elbow. I shall write nothing in detail about so-called man-eaters and others; suffice it to say that I and my associates go down month after month, scores of times, and are too much enthralled by the interest and beauty and the never-ending strangeness of it all to give a thought to possible dangers.

Dangers, that is, from the creatures of the sea. Mechanical hazards are different. With unrelaxed vigilance we watch each diver and apparatus, and it is seldom that anything goes wrong. Once an inexperienced person in the helmet snagged the hose behind a projecting branch of coral, and, thinking that the tightening of the hose was the push of the tide, fought back to the ladder. There was fortunately sufficient length to allow an approach to within three feet of the surface, when we were able to reach the helmet. If this had not been possible, one of us would have dived and pulled off the helmet in mid-water, forcing the diver to swim to the surface.

Two or three times, in spite of our care, one of the leading ropes of the launch has become untied or broken. Instantly three sharp jerks on the hose tell that something is wrong. The last time this happened I was perched twelve feet up the reef edge. I jumped to the open sand and saw the launch drifting rapidly over the reef, the ladder already hung up on a rock. I was afraid to use it, for fear of its snapping or of catching my hand between it and the reef. So I pulled the hose down until it became taut, and wrapping the loose coils about me, I cached my arrow sling and net, and went swiftly up, hand over hand, obliquely over the reef, attended by an excited mob of abudefdufs and surgeons. An anchor carried out to mid-sand in the glass-bottom dinghy enabled me to free the ladder, salvage my weapon, and resume my hunting.

As once before in Haiti I caught my ankle in a crevice of Almost Island — a diabolically ingenious tie-up which compelled my sitting still and overcoming a momentary impulse to tear loose. When I had stopped unnecessarily using up the precious air in the helmet, I set systematically to work, and after trying every kind of push and pull and compression, and going through another unpleasant moment, I twisted around to bend my arrow and use it as additional leverage, when suddenly my ankle slipped out.

The coming of night to Almost Island deserves a chapter, or if we knew even a fraction of the great changes which every evening brings, an entire volume. The setting sun gives way to blue, always blue, blackness, the movement of one's hand sets fire to a thousand luminous creatures in mid-water; many of the day-loving fish go to sleep in amazing positions; the big-eyed squirrelfish and the sinister morays come forth, and the sharks begin to work their

way in from the open sea. A sight I shall not forget is that of a
dead horse which we tied to the western buoy; at sunset Almost
Island was alive with sharks. There were dozens of the four-foot
puppy sharks which are so common about Nonsuch, and now and
then I caught a glimpse of the white belly of one much larger, as
it twisted up from below to share the feast. The next morning the
horse had disappeared, not a shark was in sight, and over the spot
five angelfish swam lazily, their golden filaments streaming out
behind — the usual peace of early morning had returned to Almost
Island.

The supreme achievement in helmet diving is "dangling," and
I do not think this word has been used so appropriately before.
The sea must be calm and without much swell and there must be
a slight offshore breeze. On the last day of this combination I
went out in the launch, beyond Gurnets, perhaps a quarter of a
mile. Usually I try to see bottom, but if the water is slightly murky
or cloud shadows are frequent, this is impossible. When I thought
we were over a suitable place, the engines were shut off, and I let
out the entire forty-five feet of ladder and started down.

In September the water is warm and fish life is at its greatest
abundance. Peering down I could see nothing but a foggy blueness
— it looked as if I were dropping off the rim of the world into
starless space. I had no feeling of bottom at all; it was a real connecting link between my Almost Island meanderings and the view
from the bathysphere, two hundred fathoms down. I stopped halfway, swung around, and found myself as if in cosmic space. There
was no sign of reef below or boat or surface overhead; I was too
close to the ladder to see them, so I was apparently suspended in
mid-ether; a cloud shut out the sun for the moment and the dusk
was eerie — unlike any earthly twilight. The fog-blue spaces swirled
past; I could actually see thinner and denser areas, probably the

shift of light from the face of the wave mirrors high overhead. I swiveled half a circle and entered a galaxy — a whole constellation of great jellyfish. *Aurelias* they were, sun jellies, but a much more appropriate term would be *Lunelias*, for they were gray and misty. Two and thirty of these active moons, all more than a foot across, throbbed around me, set at all angles, each with a quartet of bright pink loops at its center — egg masses, insurance of future generations of sun jellies. One bumped against the glass of my helmet, and before it could regain equilibrium, I reached out and held it balanced. Two or three tiny fish dashed away, and in the jelly's watery tissues I could see small crustaceans, embedded like flies in amber — parasites in a living film of water. The delicate fringe of tentacles waved about my face more gracefully than cobwebs in air. There came to me a profound feeling of the permanence of the evanescent — these one half of one per cent of life filling the ocean with their myriads, with adequate provision for the future, each jelly perfect — and I knew that the first newspaper I would open on my return would be an almost pure culture of worry, fear, danger, warning, despair. None of us wish to be "spineless jellyfish," but here was I, held fascinated by the marvel of their form and movement, and wishing for us a little of the calm and assurance of their lives.

Half a dozen more rungs brought the bottom into clear view, and now I slid slowly down until I grasped the lowermost, swung my feet and legs free in mid-water, and — *dangled*. There had been a very light breeze in the upper world when I left, and I found that I was hardly moving, drifting very slowly seaward. Within my forty-or-fifty-feet horizon all was one tumult of tortured rock — caves, gullies, slender arms of stone reaching out toward me, deep unsounded wells, galleries winding in and out — everything except a bit of flatness. I saw a great round mass slowly approaching, and soon I was able to stand upright on a mighty brain coral. I laughed a hollow, coppery laugh all to myself in my helmet at the thought of my resemblance to Gulliver, only here I was perched upon the cranium of a giant who must have been a genius, with an appalling amount of convolutions showing clearly through his skull. I was gently tipped off during my momentary amusement, and again I dangled.

The next projection was an angled bit of stone overgrown with seaweeds and plumes. While in temporary possession I danced vigorously upon it, kicked and stamped and scraped, and my reward for the next few minutes after I was plucked from it was a school of fifty golden wrasse, dashing about the disturbed debris until they reminded me of the kaleidoscope of silver wires of moonlight on water. The sun was out full strength, and against the dark rocks and weed the little fish shone like fire. As I drifted out of sight, I could see the forms of larger creatures moving toward the unexpected manna. If I derived any satisfaction from being a freak pioneer, I could boast that I was the first human being who had fed fishes by dancing on coral tops eight fathoms down!

These open-sea danglings were like looking through a magnifying glass, the coral heads were so much more massive, the plumes taller, the fish so considerably larger than those of the inshore reefs — blue surgeons and angelfish, giant butterflies, parrots over four feet, and other fish in proportion. Now and then I saw a species new to our list, or even to Bermuda, some of which will always remain unknown to me, others recognizable on sight.

Toward the end of this particular dangle, my drifting speed increased; the wind in the upper world was evidently rising. I swept past jagged ridges and deep, dark valleys; then came sand, twenty feet farther down; next an island, and more sand. Suddenly a jagged crest appeared ahead. I scrambled hastily up half a dozen rungs and prepared to pull the ladder after me. The only real danger of this work is that of the lower part of the metal ladder catching on some out-jutting finger and snapping in two or at the surface. I was constantly on the watch for such a catastrophe, hoping to be able to pull the ladder clear of the passing danger in time. In the event of its happening, the only thing to do would be to leap clear of the ladder and go hand over hand up the hose.

My ridge proved to be the last projection I could reach, and far from its catching on the ladder, I found I could only touch here and there by dangling full length, straight down from the lowest rung. Beyond lay a valley of shadows, then more sand, and my last view showed two grandfathers of all groupers, at least six feet in length, turning slowly and looking up at me. I had a moment's wild desire to let go and try to cross the sandy deserts and clamber the intervening reef mountains between me and Almost Island a quarter mile away. Then I remembered my limitations and ceased wishing to impose too great a strain upon my wonderful relations with the sea.

I climbed leisurely, my body and legs floating out behind, and again passed through the zone of star dust and *Aurelias*, and before I knew it, the helmet was whisked off, I was asked what I had seen, and at once the perfection of my inarticulate visions began to be dissected and distorted by being forced into the pitifully inadequate vehicle of human speech and writing.

CHAPTER 3

Feathered Tourists

WHEN you look for things and hope for things and greatly desire things year after year, and train your senses to continue their concentration after the less important parts of you are sleeping or eating or playing or merely talking, then, sooner or later, very special things happen within sight or hearing, smell or touch radius. I have been lucky, for a queen termite once began her miraculous city at the very moment I was crossing my compound; giant fruit bats traversed the surface of the moon just as I focused glasses on it; a Sclater's Impeyan pheasant reached the summit of a bamboo hill in northern Burma as I crept up the opposite slope; shooting stars seem often to hang back in obscurity until I am looking at their exact future path; and I have missed more than one important lob at tennis because a rare migrant drew my eye to the sky beyond.

For two days a single greater yellowlegs had lived on South Beach, Nonsuch, feeding, sleeping, and chumming with a band of turnstones and benefiting by their football rushes against the loose clumps of stranded sargassum. The third day, August 9, most of me was deep in the characters of a new species of *Pseudoscopelus*, when suddenly my ears, which were wholly unconcerned with this microscopic work, pulled all the rest of me out of my chair and rushed me outdoors. My focusing hands, my squinting eyes, my technical convolutions had no chance against the sudden aural demand — the call of a passing sandpiper being the electric spark of a sound which had sprung the mine.

Back and forth overhead swung my yellowlegs, calling as he went — then seaward. My hands needed no help in unleashing and orienting my large glasses; my eyes knew better than to leave this ventriloquial note in the wide heavens. Down along the top of the barrels I followed him, and almost without a break sighted him again, grown twelve times larger, in the lenses. I had a comfortable ledge on which to rest and swivel the glasses. Five hundred feet above the sea he encountered a stiff breeze and for many minutes fought and fought against it. He was headed due south and I knew that no land this side of Cuba or Haiti would give him rest, and yet here he was using up vitality and strength battling a wall of wind only a few hundred yards off Nonsuch. Suddenly he seemed to give up, and swung around and back in a great circle almost overhead; then the frantic pressing forward began again. If the bird had been the negative end of a compass needle, the austral pull could not have been more continuous.

Three times he circled and three times lost all he had gained, and then, as so often in my life, I realized that pity was needless, sympathy was endgendered only by human conceit, for my eyes suddenly sensed that from the moment I first saw the bird he had been gaining altitude — at first so gradually that my brain refused to record the diminution, and now more swiftly. I did not dare to wink; now and then I confused the sandpiper with some mote in my eye's circulation, but before he passed wholly and forever beyond view, I saw the last spiral straighten out, and with elemental directness, high above the stratum of head wind, he sped straight out to sea, with a strength and assurance which streamed through the last thin column of vision between the beating wings of the bird and my eye. My straining eyes compelled a wink, and there was left in my glasses only a round view of blue sky with a cottony cloud in the lower left-hand corner.

The job I had set myself on my new island home was the study of the fish of the deep sea and the shore, but I would choose any day to be a poor naturalist rather than a good ultraspecialist. So forthwith, looking ahead to other migrant birds, I built me a blind of driftwood and boxes at the hither end of the beach, between two low cedars, where I had a clear view of the shrubs, grass, sand and water which composed the hundred yards of the crescent cove.

And by the way, when age forecloses my life mortgage of activity, and I can only hobble, I shall use up a year to good advantage near a beach like this — studying and recording the amazing changes, day by day, in physical geography, in its wracks and wrecks, its seaweed, shells, jellyfish, the storm-driven pieces of broken boats, and things dropped overboard; and, far from least, the migrant birds which come, and feed, and rest, and go.

My blind, which, when finished, looked uncomfortably like a front trench dugout, was my Mecca for a short time early every morning. I found that just before sunup gave the best visibility. I began with Zeiss Number 3's, then 6's, and finally swept the beach with Number 12's, only the last had to be rested on the topmost box and swiveled like a machine gun. Each glass spoiled me for the preceding, and one day I completed my optical downfall and laid up bad trouble ahead. I see, in the future, times of muscle agony, of weary, overladen tramps through swamps, through bitter cold, through blistering heat — scores of times of physical exhaustion but mental and emotional ecstasy — all because I was tempted to lug my giant telescope-binoculars down to the beach. They are

Brobdingnagian opera glasses, mighty double-barrels, weighing 16 pounds, each tube 22 inches long, and with revolving eyepieces of 12, 20, and 40 diameters.

I set them up on the tripod, arranged a comfortable seat, and focused. For two score years I have been peering at wild birds through glasses of one kind or another, but one glance now and I realized that I had never yet really seen a wild bird. The 12-power eyepiece gave me the same magnification as my largest field glasses, which, as I have said, are too powerful to use satisfactorily without a rest. But here the illumination was almost of the naked eye in full sunlight. Then I turned the 20-power into alignment, and it is a wonder that my exclamation did not clear the beach of bird life.

The naked eye saw a confused group too far away for certain identification; the Number 3's permitted recognition of all but the smaller sandpipers; but through the twin telescopes the field was completely filled by a quartet of turnstones, a sanderling, and two semipalmated sandpipers. Never satisfied, I turned on the 40 diameters but could not get a clear focus — I was too close! After all, this was a telescope, not a hand lens.

I found that from my laboratory porch on Nonsuch I could focus on Castle Island, which was over 1300 yards, or three quarters of a mile, away, and with a favorable light could readily distinguish between the sexes of house sparrows and even of bluebirds. On Brangman's, a quarter of a mile off, I could detect the most delicate coloring of bills, feet, and eyes, and could identify any species of Bermuda butterfly.

With or without my telescope I kept South Beach under observation for six migration seasons — three north and three southward. This beach is the only one hereabouts which is sheltered and yet faces the open ocean. It receives more sargassum weed than any other, and this indirectly brings the migrants, for the weed offers shelter and nursery facilities to the little *Orchestia*, or sand hoppers, which, on Nonsuch, run the sun a close second as the source of life.

In the course of three years I have observed seventeen species of shore birds, all migrants, on South Beach. Seven of these I saw only once or twice — phalaropes, dowitchers, yellowlegs, willets, Hudsonian curlews, and black-bellied and golden plovers.

Nine birds were seen frequently enough to be called regular annual visitors. Six of these were sandpipers, least, semipalmated, sanderlings, greater yellowlegs, solitary and spotted; two were plovers, semipalmated and piping; and the most abundant were the turnstones.

At first, to make sure of certain identifications, I shot a few birds, until there was no question of easy recognition at sight, and on days when no rare species appeared, I studied the regulars as species personalities. All the birds I shot I found to be stuffed with the sand-hopping amphipods which lived in the seaweed, but the thing that interested me most was the inorganic contents of the small gizzards. One could always become emotional when a tired migrant swung into view and landed on the beach. One thought how the fluff of feathers had fought wind and darkness and the ever-present danger of the imminent waves for hundreds of miles from the last take-off to this speck of land in mid-Atlantic. But when I tumbled the grit from the gizzards out upon my microscope stage and focused it, and turned over the little particles with my finger, I made much more than a theoretical contact with the arctic homes of these birds. In the turnstones and the least and semipalmated sandpipers, mingled with the remains of the crustaceans I found tiny bits of stone — fair rocks and boulders they looked under the lens — not the ground-up shell and sand grains and comminuted armor of crab and snail which compose the strand of Bermuda, but rounded bits of granite and glassy quartz, and red, pitted, hematitelike minerals, here and there a bit rough and black like lava. From Melville Bay, northern Labrador, the Yukon's mouth, these came — and the scant six inches of least sandpiper brought his from Ungava, Yakutat Bay, Keewatin, and perhaps the farthest point of northwestern Alaska — four thousand miles and more away. Here in my mid-Atlantic laboratory I was fingering the very soil itself from these magic lands of the north, brought to me in the bodies of the shore birds. Once getting the full meaning of this, I shot no more birds during my whole stay. There was no need — my telescope brought them all out of the conventional bush and placed them in my hand.

The moment we take to ourselves a bird as a pet, it becomes an individual and acquires a personality, and only one who has had to do with the building of a zoo can possibly appreciate the mental and emotional gulfs separating two feathered creatures which, to the eye, are absolutely identical.

In watching my wild birds, I found that with varying magnifications I could pass through several stages of optical intimacy. To the naked eye, as I have said, the shore birds on the farther side of the beach were only a group of wading birds, but even with the lowest-power glasses there began to emerge what may be called the species behavior, or specific personality, quite apart from color and pattern, and even size. For example, an eighth day of September, when there were many kinds of waders on the beach, I made the following action and psychological key, which, when given to members of my staff to use, proved as effective for identification as details of color and size revealed through much higher magnifications.

SPOTTED SANDPIPER: *Comparatively deliberate, not at all wary, the rather stout body constantly teetering.*

SEMIPALMATED SANDPIPER: *Nervous but not wary, moving in short, running spurts, pecking but seldom, always retrieving a morsel of food, constantly fighting or pretending courtship.*

LEAST SANDPIPER: *Very tame, seldom on guard, movements more irregular than preceding, pecking constantly, only now and then finding and swallowing food, never fighting, often taking advantage of turnstones' activities in uncovering food.*

SANDERLING: *Constantly drilling deep holes, one after another, seldom merely pecking, usually near water line.*

TURNSTONE: *A waddling walk, feeding by pushing weed over, butting it with the head.*

PIPING PLOVER: *Timid, nervous, large eyes never off guard, snatching food quickly, near water; time spent watching to time of feeding, about 20 to 1.*

SEMIPALMATED PLOVER: *Still more timid, long intervals of watching, feeds higher up the beach, at every stop one leg lifted very slightly.*

Some day we will know more about these phases of animal life — where the spirit of the flock merges into specific personality, and when and why this, in turn, gives way to the unrestricted interplay of individual emotions and mental reactions.

The turnstones were the most abundant and regular beach birds. It seems settled that they do not breed in Bermuda, yet they are the earliest to arrive and the last to be seen. Three notes from my journal reveal an interesting happening — all the more inexplicable if all the birds are migrants.

September 7, 1929 — Seventeen turnstones on South Beach, two of which are cripples. One, a female, has the right foot bent far over and stiffened. The other is a male and has lost the entire right foot, toes and metatarsus, the limb having healed at the tarsal joint. The plucky bird balances perfectly and stumps easily about, feeding and holding its own in every way. Strangest of all, its fellows often quarrel among themselves over a rich find of sand hoppers, but all give way to the cripple.

June 7, 1930 — Nine turnstones on South Beach, one of them the identical cripple seen a year ago, a male in normal plumage.

May 17,1931 — Three cripples among a flock of ten birds. Two of these I saw in 1929 and one last year. Diagrams I made at the time of the peculiar arrangement of the inbent toes of the female and of a hardened, inward-projecting flap of skin seen at the stump of the male's leg leave no possibility of doubt of the individual identity.

August 17, 1931 — Of four turnstones, three are cripples, one a new one with the left leg hanging loose, swinging about, so the bird has either to hop or squat flat. It is a male in good plumage, and feeds as well as a normal bird. The tarsal-stump male is the same seen in 1929 and 1930.

We know how the slightest handicap of abnormal structure or even color is usually soon fatal to a bird, slain either by keen-eyed hawk or by the savage assaults of its own kind. Yet here were birds migrating year after year, holding their own and undisturbed by members of their flock — cripples with a distorted foot, a dislocated upper leg, or actual loss of one leg.

I have never seen these birds pragmatize their name, probably because I have never observed them on a rocky beach, but here they eternally merit the name Turnweeds. While far less dainty and trim and graceful in outline and gait than the other shore birds, yet their plumage is always immaculate and undisturbed, and as far as actual beauty of pattern and brilliance of pigment go, their harlequin rufous, black and white plumage is supreme among the birds of the beach. Yet alone among all of their relatives they spend most of their time butting and pushing and shoving against the half-dried sargassum weed, in spite of which, with the most powerful glasses, I can never see a disarranged feather on their foreheads or a dirty or bedraggled plume on breast or wing. This unique habit of searching for and finding food brings about very definite relations with many of the other birds.

The scene on October 3 well illustrated this. A fairly strong northeast wind was blowing from inland across the beach, and this, plus a hard-working shock troop of turnstones, resulted in an amusing interrelationship of the birds in sight. Six turnstones were crowded in the lee of a great stranded log, all butting and straining, head down, at the windrow of weed. They of course reaped a rich harvest. The birds were less than two hundred feet away, and with my 20-powers I could readily distinguish even the varying colors of the cloud of sand hoppers which arose at each rolling over of a bunch of weed. The beaks of the turnstones worked like pistons, each downthrust representing the diminution of the race of *Orchestia platensis* by one. These unfortunately overedible little beings have themselves traveled far over the world, probably clinging to weed and driftwood, and today they range from Nova Scotia to Brazil and are also at home on the shores of the Mediterranean.

As the turnstones rolled their weed on this windy day, hundreds of the sand hoppers leaped so high into the air that they were caught by the wind and carried down over the white sand. Four leasts, a semipalmated and sanderling scurried and ran, first rushing up close to the log, then, as a barrage of hoppers passed overhead, they would fan out and tear down the beach, chasing and finally capturing the particular game they had selected. I could tell the direction and the number of leaps of the crustacean by the dodging and stops of the feathered hunter. Now and then a particularly sporting *Orchestia* would leap and be wind-blown to the very ocean's edge, when one of the sandpipers would wade into the ripples breast-high to retrieve it.

Low down on the beach a solitary cool-gray piping plover and an equally exquisite and dainty semipalmated plover fed in their timid way. They were too dignified to chase sand hoppers. With my telescope I could see every feather, every fearful glance of their great eyes, and could even detect the three kinds of worms which they were unholing. The belted plover would have made friends and tried to feed close to his paler cousin, but the piper would have none of it and missed many a toothsome worm by constant pursuit of his fellow.

On a windless day when the birds spray out more along the beach, each turnstone has an attendant pair or trio of sandpiper camp followers. The leasts are the most impudent and fearless. They fairly get between the legs of the turnstones and dash in at the first hint of moving weed, as the larger birds brace themselves to shift it. The other sandpipers hang about the outskirts of the gastronomic game of rugby, but none ever learns to butt or push the weed aside for himself. It is as exclusive a characteristic of the turnstones as their bandy gait and parti-colored feathers.

On Nonsuch we have a radio which we never use, a telephone which functions only in case of vital need; papers from the outside world reach us a week late and no one minds. Our work is too absorbing seriously to miss contact with the rest of the planet, but when the last tropic bird leaves its home in the cliffs, and the ultimate crippled turnstone rises from the beach and sets its course out to sea, Nonsuch becomes a little desolate. We cherish our sea birds and we love our tourists in feathers.

CHAPTER 4

Cahows and Longtails

NIGHT after night, throughout all the spring months we have been here, when dark closes down, there come through the murk from the direction of the open sea strange voices — sweet, modulated tones wholly unlike the metallic *pink!* or *tink!* of the tropic birds. The calls are harmonious with no element of harshness, half tones following whole tones, while occasionally there rings out a trisyllabic, silvery minor chord: *whee-o! whee-whee-o!* I have wondered often at these disembodied Sirens, and finally I began to box them on the horizon of my blind, auditory compass. They came consistently from a narrow sector in the southeast, and after a few nights of confirmatory repetition I shifted my observations one morning to a visible horizon and found that the source of the nocturnal voices included Green Island — the last continuation of Nonsuch beyond South Point.

During the first year of my stay I had wandered over this small, isolated, wave-worn patch which was about one hundred yards across and had found nothing of especial interest. On the sixteenth of May we visited it again. I leaped from the stern of a small boat as it balanced upon the summit of a rising swell, and swarmed up a cliff composed of effectively arranged serried ranks of pins,

daggers, needles, half-opened scissors, knives, nails, fishhooks, arrows and bits of broken glass. It proved, after all, to be only a cliff
of aeolian sand, dissolved and refused and tempered to marble
hardness, and sculptured and whetted to razor sharpness by the
waves, but to hands and feet it was all the rest. The islet rose to a
low, central table rock by way of two diminutive and irregular ter-
races, and its title was saved from absolute misnomer solely by a
thin emerald enamel of flattened and sprawling sea purslane with
its tiny, purplish-pink faces staring up at the sky. Single and double
pads of island cactus hid low among the scattered sea oxeye and
marine mulberry. No cedar today has been able to face the blasting
salt and live, although stony molds here and there showed where
great forests had stood on the island in unknown times past.

We had hardly begun to quarter the islet, when, on the very
summit, thrown up by a breaker during some mighty storm, we
found a pair of wings joined by the ivory-white shoulder girdle of
some small sea bird. Then our search was stimulated by the discovery of a bit of white eggshell far under a low ledge. A triumphant shout summoned me to the extreme southerly tip. Centuries
upon centuries ago, when Nonsuch Bay was encircled by dry land,
one of the greatest of cedars reared its foliage upon this spot. All
that remained in this twentieth hundredth year of our calendar
was the limestone outline of the trunk and large roots, all the details of the weathered contours being still distinct. It was easy to
trace the meandering of the roots, to see where a mighty twist
had been taken about some helping shoulder of rock — a rock long
since dissolved — the straining of the plant muscles, which began
ages before the time of the Egyptians, being still visible in the sunlight of today.

The great mineral bole stood up nearly three feet above the rest
of the surface of the island, and when I came closer, I saw it was

hollow. I peered down, and after the excitement of bright sunlight had died down in my eyes, I discerned in the heart of this marble tree the softest thing in the world — a downy chick. It was almost the hue of the twilight in which it lived and was cozily squatting beneath a low, half-open ceiling of rock tracery. As I looked something equally dark scuffled into view, and my chick gave forth a series of high protesting cheeps as it wriggled from beneath the feet of its nervous mother. She turned a shining black eye up at me and waited for what this new adventure might bring forth. I could see her only in sections, and what was visible led my ornithological mind first to sooty terns, then to Mother Carey's chickens.

We made certain that there was no half-hidden exit and that she must clamber up and down the hollow chimney of the prehistoric cedar. Then we found that it was impossible to reach her. Whenever I lowered my hand and arm, she shuffled back a few inches and was as safe as if behind the strongest of steel bars. Only a mighty charge of dynamite would have dislodged her, while all I wanted was to make identification certain. The age of the young bird ensured another week or two of habitation, so we left with reasonable hopes of seeing them again.

The sector of the aural compass extended somewhat to the east of Green Island, so on the following day we landed on Idol Island. This is separated from Nonsuch by a narrow strait through which the tide flows back and forth in a restless stream fifteen feet in width. It is even smaller than Green Island — possibly one hundred feet across — and on the summit rises in solitary grandeur the stone idol which dominates the lacerating surface. Its expression and even its personality vary when viewed from different points along the Nonsuch shore, and I have named five successive promontories after the gods whose profiles are suggested — Chubu, Buddha, Kib, Anubis, Hanuman.

This islet I found the metropolis of these birds. They proved to be dusky, or Audubon, shearwaters, and are to Bermuda what the flightless cormorant is to Albemarle, and the heath hen to Martha's Vineyard — a bird on the point of extinction. Fossil remains of this and a very closely related petrel have been found in crevices and caves of all the surrounding islands. I have unearthed, or rather unsanded, a half dozen on Nonsuch.

On this tiny Idol Island I found five successes and five failures among the shearwater nests. On my first visit a parent bird was sitting on an empty nest; next time both birds were present; and the third time the crevice was vacant. Two white eggs discovered the first time were later found to be deserted, although one was about to hatch and the other was fresh. Two downy young with no parents to guard them during the day grew apace and at last flew safely away, and a third young bird which was constantly attended by one parent also survived. One shearwater had chosen a nesting place in a deep crevice which could not possibly be reached, but by sighting through lateral slits, I watched the young bird and saw it last just before it climbed up the narrow chimney and flew. Finally an easily accessible shearwater was found on a half-grown young. It was lifted up, examined, measured carefully and replaced; and it successfully reared the youngster.

The young birds were a pure culture of mouse-gray fluff, with no visible feet, only a negligible glint of an eye, and a wholly inadequate beak. They were paler below, but the dark gray of the upper parts was exactly the color of the weathered rocks. The parents were simply and severely black above and pure white on the side of the head and all the underparts. The eggs were the only conspicuous thing in the entire life of these birds — whitest of white.

Three weeks later when I swam through the rush of waters and crept up the sharp rocks of Idol Island, I found the youngsters rather disheveled, still downy superficially but with the real feathers well started beneath and the wings sprouting rapidly. They were almost bald, the pin feathers of the scalp having started growth. They were fluffed out and looked obese and at least twice the size of the parents.

I have already mentioned the numerous remains of half-fossiled bones of these small petrels on all surrounding islands from Castle to St. David's, attesting their former abundance — bones of two species, of one of which only a single mounted specimen remains. Today I have heard Bermudian fishermen speak of these voices of the night as cahows, and the early settlers of these islands knew both species by this name.

Going back more than three centuries, one William Strachy on the fifteenth of July, 1610, wrote as follows concerning these little sea birds:

A kind of webbe-footed Fowle there is, of the bigness of an English green Plouer, or Sea-Meawe, which all the Summer wee saw not, and in the darkest nights of Nouember and December (for in the night they only feed) they would come forth, but not flye farre from home, and houering in the ayre, and oure the Sea, made a strange hollow and harsh howling. Their color is inclining to Russet, with white bellies, as are likewise the long Feathers of their wings Russet and White, these gather themselues together and breed in those Ilands which are high, and so farre alone into the Sea, that the Wilde Hogges cannot swimme ouer them, and there in the ground they haue their Burrowes, like Conyes in a Warren, and so brought in the loose Mould, though not so deepe; which Birds with a light bough in a darge night (as in our Lowbelling) wee caught. I have beene at the taking of three hundred in an houre, and wee might haue laden our Boates. Our men found a prettie way to take them, which was by standing on the Rockes or Sands by the Sea side, and hollow-

ing, laughing, and making the strangest out-cry that possibly they could; with the noyse whereof the Birds would come flocking to that place, and settle vpon the very armes and head of him that so cryed, and still creepe neerer and neerer, answering the noyse themselues: by which our men would weigh them with their hand, and which weighed heauiest they tooke for the best, and let the others alone, and so our men would take twentie dozen in two houres of the chiefest of them: and they were a good and well relished Fowle, fat and full as a partridge. In January wee had great store of their Egges, which are great as an Hennes Egge, and so fashioned and white shelled, and haue no difference in yolke nor white from an Hennes Egge. There are thousands of these birds, and two or three Ilands full of their Burrowes, whether at any time (in two hours warning) wee could send our Cockboat, and bringe home as many as would serue the whole Company: which birds for their blindnesse (for they see weekly in the day) and for their cry and whooting, we called Sea Owl; they will bite cruelly with their crooked Bills.

And now tonight in the late evening of June 7, 1931, three hundred and twenty-one years later, I sit, probably within sight of the place where William wrote his excellent account, and there come to my ears the plaintive calls of the last of the cahows. They may cling to their pitiful islet crevices for a few more years, for collecting ornithologists are rare in Bermuda, laws are strict, caretakers are vigilant, and the difficulty and danger of making a landing on these wave-beaten outer islands is considerable. The cahow will forever remain to me as one of my successful pursuits of a sound in the night.

One day I chose to sit in the heart of a hollow caldron of great boulders at the foot of a western cliff on Nonsuch. Purple, green — purple, green; the ocean stretches out beyond the jagged barrier in front, in successive streaks of violent color. The horizon is clear except for the stegosauruslike bulk of Gurnets Head a half mile off. Not quite clear, however, for my eye catches a tiny dot, a less than period — our tug *Gladisfen* at the vanishing point of sea and sky, drawing her two miles of slender tentacle thread, with the sextet of tiny pocket nets, through the cold blackness of the lower ocean.

To my left towers a massive arch carved out by wind and water and framing a vista of cliff and sea and distant cedars. Not far away are two other arches long since fallen in, and I look up at the weakest point of the colossal curve overhead and wonder whether I will be allowed to complete this sentence. Somewhere in its substance there is the deciding grain of sand; somewhere a certain wave is gathering strength; in some imminent or distant time-space a gentle wind is arising. At the appointed time, when all these three shall meet, the wave will splash up and loosen the grain of sand, the wind will blow it from its age-old support, and gravitation, patient gravitation, will have its way. Whether it happens before this page is completed and uncounted tons of rock bury these eyes, hand and paper, or whether some successor ten thousand years from now will be enabled suddenly to cease worrying about the petty things of his life is of no importance. It is only certain that then, as now, tropic birds quite indistinguishable from those of today will rush for the last time through the arch and hover excitedly over the fallen debris.

(On July 15, three weeks after this was written, an outer shelf above the arch fell and killed a tropic bird. A few days later I dug out the bird and found a downy nestling which had died of starvation in an inner hollow. This was the first tragedy of the arch — an infinitesimal inorganic climax bringing to a close one of the topmost twigs of the tree of organic evolution.)

Even more than hummingbirds, tropic birds are beings of the

air. Infinitely more than the birds of paradise do they deserve the name *Apodes*, for neither legs nor feet are clearly to be seen and are used as little as possible.

In flight two small patches are visible flattened below against the base of the tail — the webbed toes tucked out of the way. They are hardly more in evidence when the owner alights on the water or when it enters its nest. Like the landing of an overweighted airplane, the entering of the nesting hole by a tropic bird is a serious affair. Three or four false attempts are usually made before the trajectory and speed are adjusted to the wind and the parti-colored chassis is deposited on a slight ledge or actually in the hole. The bird then wriggles and pushes forward, seallike, until it disappears.

One of the most useless characters I can imagine is the long, attenuated central pair of tail feathers. It surely can be of no courtship value, for these birds court and mate in mid-air, almost always two males in fierce rivalry. Under these circumstances it is difficult to imagine any nice adjustment as to admired length, resiliency, or sweep of the feathery ornaments. The plumes are exceedingly tough and rubbery, as they must be to resist the wear and tear of constant attrition against the narrow ledges and rocky tunnels.

The yellow-billed tropic bird is virtually the only sea bird that nests in Bermuda, a fact wholly unreasonable to our human minds. For here are hosts of perfect nesting places on isolated islets and unclimbable cliffs; here is food — crabs, fish, squid — in abundance; and, most important in these later days of evolution, here are ironclad man-made laws to protect them. Yet gulls and terns, gannets and petrels hesitate or alight only to recover from stress of storms, and then go their way to Greenland or to Patagonia, according to the season's urge.

The tropic birds call cousins such diverse beings as pelicans, snakebirds, cormorants and man-o'-war birds, and their voice is as unlike these as their bodies. The chronic syrinx abortion of the adult pelican leaves him only a sibilant hiss of air passing over untuned chords; the cormorants grunt and croak like frogs; the man-o'-war has a courtship cadenza liquid as a songbird's; but the trio of passing tropic birds sends down to me only a harsh, metallic *tink! tink!* recalling the flock notes of crossbills coming over a snowfield, or tree frogs tinkling in the dusk of a tropical jungle.

Longtail is the Bermudian name for these black and white birds. They seem to change color as rapidly as the squid upon which they feed, for when they fly over our whitewashed laboratory roof, their breasts are as immaculate as snow; over the shallows their plumage takes on the faintest, most delicate of pale chrysoprase; and far out from land, where the water draws its color from a full-mile depth of ocean, reflection touches the plumage with a bubble-thin tint of ultramarine. When we see a tropic bird in full plumage on its nest in sunlight, within arm's length, a new color impinges upon our retina; we can no longer call its breast and tail white, and we cannot say that they are salmon or pink; the delicacy of this new real tone survives no human-made name — it is sheer beauty.

In early March the tropic birds appear, and the fishermen know that all the squid will vanish, solely, as they think, because of the arrival of their dominant enemies. But somewhere there are still squid in abundance, for the crops of the birds bulge with them, caught far out at sea, and the young are fed chiefly on squid as well as flying fish.

There must be some significance in the constant sight of three birds flying together. It seems possible that there are more females than males, and that bigamy is not an uncommon event. On the other hand, fierce battles are waged over the females, and I have sent my photographer to a ledge where two birds had been lying for a half hour, beak grasped by beak, wings bent and twisted beneath their bodies as they tumbled about or lay in angry exhaustion. They paid no attention to the man when he photographed them, and he finally picked them up and tore them apart. Even when both had been tossed out into the air, they immediately resumed the battle on the wing.

They seem tireless in flight, and I have rarely seen them resting upon the water. Ten miles out at sea a solitary bird will now and then appear and swoop low over the tug, dipping his ensign to his fellow neighbors of Nonsuch. Then he resumes his chiefest, but one, duty in life — his search for food — and when this is found, he broad-arrows his whole being, and with gravitation for impetus, shoots down upon squid or fish. Such mastery over the air and sea have these tropic birds that it is less wonderful that they control their inner selves. The squid may be swallowed and digested at once. Or if it is intended as sustenance for mate or offspring, it can be stored in the gullet. Hours later when it is decanted into the maw of the young bird, it is as fresh as when newly caught.

As one walks along the cliff edge of Nonsuch or clambers up and down the diminutive canyons and badlands near the water, a vocal mine is sprung now and then, apparently beneath one's feet — a sudden, unexpected, screeching, unoiled rattle which startles the calmest nerves. This is a parent tropic bird objecting with raucous protest to the invasion of her domain. The nearest crevice or tunnel shows her flashing eyes and her yellow beak half open, ready for able defense. We nudge her to one side, and the immaculate contour of her breast is disturbed by a segment of purplish-brown egg, or through the white feathers there pops a tiny head only less white because of the fluffiness of its down. Here we have an epitome of tropic-bird development.

The parent explodes again and the downy infant echoes her in a weak and minor key. But there is a marked individuality, and I have lifted some birds off their nest, examined and replaced them without eliciting a sound of remonstrance.

For two successive years on Nonsuch (1929 and 1930) there were fifty-seven occupied nests within climbing reach and probably thirty more on the northern cliffs beyond human approach. I banded parents with green and nestlings with red leg bands and found that the young breed the second year, and, in a few cases at least, the same birds return to the same nesting holes.

Some of the nests were in exquisite positions, such as one little cave with three entrances divided from each other by marble columns or completed stalactites, with overhanging flowering vines partly shielding the aperture. When the parent was absent one day, I climbed down from above, took a firm toe grip on a branch, and let myself down until my head was well inside the hollow. The view through the vines and arched ways was very lovely, even upside down as I saw it and with a longtail chick thumping my nape. Lest we are tempted to endow tropic birds with aesthetic tendencies, let us remember the deep, dark, ill-smelling tunnels which form most of their homes, and realize that safety and accessiblity are the real requisites.

Sometimes at midnight I have slipped out under the stars, made my way very carefully along the south shore path, and lying flat on a jagged ridge, listened intently. Before long there would come to my ears a subdued cheeping or a deeper note, and I knew that deep within the stone below me were tropic birds and their chick, contentedly murmuring whatever tropic birds murmur at midnight.

And I thought of Nonsuch not as my laboratory, nor even as one of the most beautiful of the Somers Isles, but as a great rugged pile of marble, with the hearts of twice one hundred birds beating deep within — birds which, three months hence, would be scattered far and wide over tropical waters.

CHAPTER 5

A First Round Trip
To Davy Jones's Locker

A certain day and hour and second are approaching rapidly when a human face will peer out through a tiny window and signals will be passed back to companions, or to breathlessly waiting hosts on earth, with such sentences as:

We are above the level of Everest.
Can now see the whole Atlantic coastline.
Clouds blot out the earth.
Temperature and air pressure have dropped to minus minus.
Can see the whole circumference of Earth.
The moon appears ten times its usual size.
We now . . .

Both by daylight and by moonlight I have looked from a plane down on the earth from a height of over four miles, so I know the first kindergarten sensations of such a trip. But until I actually am enclosed within some futuristic rocket and start on a voyage into interstellar space, I shall never experience such a feeling of complete isolation from the surface of the planet Earth as when I first dangled in a hollow pea on a swaying cobweb a quarter of a mile below the deck of a ship rolling in mid-ocean.

We were able to adumbrate the above imaginary news items from a rocket mounting into interplanetary space by the following actual messages sent from the bathysphere up our telephone wire:

We have just splashed below the surface.	
We are at our deepest helmet dive.	*60 feet*
The Lusitania is resting at this level.	*285 feet*
This is the greatest depth reached in a regulation suit by Navy divers.	*306 feet*
We are passing the deepest submarine record.	*383 feet*
The Egypt was found at this level by divers in rigid shells.	*400 feet*
A diver in an armored suit descended this far into a Bavarian lake — the deepest point which a live human has ever reached.	*525 feet*
Only dead men have sunk below this.	*600 feet*
We are still alive and one quarter of a mile down.	*1426 feet*

A young gale blew itself out, and on June 3, 1930, the sun rose on a calm, slowly heaving sea. On Nonsuch Island we ran up the prearranged flag signal, and the working crew saw it from St. George's and put out. On this day we only made a trial submergence, with the bathysphere empty, to test the working of the crew and the whole apparatus.

It was let down 2000 feet, averaging two minutes for each 100 feet. Two clamps were attached, fastening the rubber hose to the cable every 200 feet. When the cable began to come in, we found there were several turns of the hose about the cable. It was beyond our power to revolve the cable, so we were compelled to remove the clamps and let the hose drop down, still twisted. As more and more clamps were removed, the ascent became increasingly difficult, the rubber hose becoming a regular snarl. By great good luck we were able to push the tangle down and down until at last the bathysphere itself appeared and we got it aboard. Draped and looped about and below it were forty-five twists of the half mile of rubber hose. We imagined the contained light and telephone wires bent and broken, and our entire venture seemed to be at an end. It looked as if we were to pay penalty at the very start for daring to attempt to delve into forbidden depths.

The crew went to work, and within twenty-four hours the half mile of hose was again neatly arranged in its great loops on the deck; and when we tested the four wires, we found the electric circuit was unbroken, light and sound passing through as perfectly as before the catastrophe.

When we wound the great steel cable onto the winch on deck from the wooden spool on which it came from the factory, without our knowing it, there must have been a slow twisting. This was not apparent until we let down the bathysphere and began attaching the rubber hose. Little by little the cable unwound, carrying around with it the pliable hose, until, when the cable was hanging straight and quiet, it had revolved forty-five times. On subsequent dives the cable never made a single turn, and the two elements came up as they went down.

June 6 was another day of almost perfect calm with only a long, heaving swell in mid-ocean. We were on board the barge early, and as soon as the tug *Gladisfen* came alongside, took her towrope, described a circle around the reefs, and headed out to sea through Castle Roads. The great jagged cliffs towered high on both sides, and on their summits the ruined battlements of the old forts frowned down upon us. I wondered what old Governor Richard Moore would have said, three hundred-odd years ago, leaning his elbows on the parapet, if he could have watched our strange procession steaming past. In all likelihood, the steaming part would have mystified and interested him far more than our chief object.

As we cleared the outer head of Brangman's, we felt the first gentle heave and settling of the swell of the ocean, and in a few minutes the foam-ringed mass of Gurnets Rock passed astern, and we steered south straight into the open sea. An hour later the angle of the two lighthouses showed that we were about eight miles off shore, with a generous mile of water beneath us. Choosing a favorable spot under such conditions is like looking around and trying to decide on the exact location of the North Pole. I think it was Dooley who said that finding the North Pole was like sitting down on the ice anywhere. And so I felt when they all awaited my signal to stop. I looked about, could detect no unusually favorable swell or especially satisfying wave, so resorted to a temporal decision and exactly at nine o'clock ordered the *Gladisfen* to stop. We headed upwind and upswell and lowered the bathysphere again with only a motion-picture camera inside. At a depth of 1500 feet this was exposed by electricity and the sphere pulled up after an hour and a half of submersion. There was nothing visible on the film, and, what was of far greater interest to us, we found not a single twist of the hose, the windows were intact, and only a quart of water was collected in the bottom.

We dried and cleaned the sphere thoroughly, then put in the oxygen tanks and the chemicals. There were two wire racks for holding the latter, one for calcium chloride for absorbing moisture, the other for soda lime for removing the excess of carbon dioxide from the air. Finally we were all ready, and I looked around at the sea and sky, the boats and my friends, at John Tee-Van and Jocelyn Crane, and not being able to think of any pithy saying which might echo down the ages, I said nothing, crawled painfully over the steel bolts, fell inside, and curled up on the cold, hard bottom of the sphere. This aroused me to speech, and I called for a cushion only to find that we had none on hand. Otis Barton climbed in after me, and we disentangled our legs and got set. I had no idea that there was so much room in the inside of a sphere only four and a half feet in diameter, and although the longer we were in it the smaller it seemed to get, yet, thanks to our adequate physique, we had room and to spare. At Barton's suggestion I took up my position at the windows, while he hitched himself over to the side of the door, where he could keep watch on the various instruments. He also put on the earphones.

Miss Hollister on deck took charge of the other end of the telephone and arranged the duplicate-control electric light so that she could watch it. Mr. Tee-Van assumed control of the deck crew.

At our signal, the four-hundred-pound door was hoisted and clanged into place, sliding snugly over the ten great steel bolts. Then the huge nuts were screwed on. If either of us had had time to be nervous, this would have been an excellent opportunity — carrying out Poe's idea of being sealed up not all at once, but little by little. For after the door was securely fastened, there remained a four-inch round opening in the center through which we could see and talk and just slip a hand. Then this mighty bolt was screwed in place, and there began the most infernal racket I have ever heard. It was necessary, not only to screw the nuts down hard, but to pound the wrenches with hammers to take up all possible slack. I was sure the windows would be cracked, but having forcibly expressed our feelings through the telephone, we gradually got used to the ear-shattering reverberations. Then utter silence settled down.

I turned my attention to the windows, cleaned them thoroughly, and tested the visual angles which I could attain by pressing my face close to the surface. I could see a narrow sector of the deck with much scurrying about, and as we rolled, I caught sight of the ultramarine sea and the *Gladisfen* dipping at the end of the slack towrope. Faint scuffling sounds reached us now and then and an occasional hollow beating. Then it seemed as if the steel walls fell away and we were again free among our fellows, for a voice came down the half mile of hose coiled on the deck, and, such is the human mind, that slender vocal connection seemed to restore physical as well as mental contact. While waiting for the take-off, Barton readjusted the phone, tested the searchlight, and opened the delicate oxygen valve. He turned it until we both verified the flow as two liters a minute — that being the amount suggested to us for two people. I remembered what I had read of Houdini's method of remaining in a closed coffin for a long time, and we both began conscientiously regulating our breathing and conversing in low tones.

Another glance through my porthole showed Tee-Van looking for a signal from old Captain Millet. I knew that now it was actually a propitious wave, or rather, a propitious lack of one, for which they waited. Soon Millet waved his hand, and exactly at one o'clock the winch grumbled, the wire on the deck tightened, and we felt our circular home tremble, lean over, and lift clear. Up we went to the yardarm, then a half score of the crew pulled with all their might and swung us out over the side. This all between two big, heaving swells. We were dangling in mid-air, and slowly we revolved until I was facing in toward the side of the *Ready*. And now our quartz windows played a trick on us. Twice already, in an experimental test submergence, we had not gauged correctly the roll of the ship or the distance outboard and the sphere had crashed into the half-rotten bulwarks. Now as I watched, I saw us begin to swing, and my eyes told me that we were much too close, and that a slightly heavier roll would crash us, windows first, into the side of the vessel. Barton could not see the imminent danger, and the next message I got was, "Gloria wants to know why the Director is swearing so." By this time we had swung far out, and I realized that every word which we spoke to each other in our tiny hollow chamber was clearly audible at the other end of the wire. I sent up word that any language was justifiable at such gross neglect as to allow our window to swing back and forth only a yard from the boat. And very decisively the word came back that fifteen feet was the nearest it had ever been, and we were now twenty-five feet away. Barton looked out with me and we could not believe our eyes. Fused quartz, as I have said, is the clearest, the most transparent material in the world, and the side of the *Ready* seemed only a yard away. My apologies must have cost us several liters of good oxygen.

To avoid any further comment on our part, profane or otherwise, we were lowered 20 feet. I sensed the weight and sturdy resistance of the bathysphere more at this moment than at any other time. We were lowered gently, but we struck the surface with a splash which would have crushed a rowboat like an eggshell. Yet within we hardly noticed the impact, until a froth of foam and bubbles surged up over the glass and our chamber was dimmed to a pleasant green. We swung quietly while the first hose clamp was put on the cable. At the end of the first revolution the great hull of the barge came into view. This was a familiar landscape which I had often seen from the diving helmet — a transitory, swaying reef with waving banners of seaweed, long tubular sponges, jet-black blobs of ascidians, and tissue-thin plates of rough-spined pearl shells. Then the keel passed slowly upward, becoming one with the green water overhead.

With this passed our last visible link with the upper world; from now on we had to depend on distant spoken words for knowledge of our depth, or speed, or the weather, or the sunlight, or anything having to do with the world of air on the surface of the earth.

A few seconds after we lost sight of the hull of the *Ready*, word came down the hose that we were at 50 feet, and I looked out at the brilliant bluish-green haze and could not realize that this was almost my limit in the diving helmet. Then "one hundred feet" was called out, and still the only change was a slight twilighting and chilling of the green. As we sank slowly, I knew that we must be passing the 132-foot level, the depth where Commander Ellsberg labored so gallantly to free the men in the Submarine S–57. "Two hundred feet" came, and we stopped with the slightest possible jerk and hung suspended while a clamp was attached — a double-gripping bit of brass which bound the cable and hose together to prevent the latter from breaking by its own weight. Then the call came that all was clear, and again I knew that we were sinking, although only by the upward passing of small motes of life in the water.

We were now very far from any touch of Mother Earth — ten miles south of the shore of Bermuda, and one and a half miles from the sea bottom far beneath us. At 300 feet, Barton gave a sudden exclamation and I turned the flash on the door and saw a slow trickle of water beneath it. About a pint had already collected in the bottom of the sphere. I wiped away the meandering stream and still it came. There flashed across my mind the memory of gentle rain falling on a windowpane and the first drops finding their way with difficulty over the dry surface of the glass. Then I looked out through the crystal-clear quartz at the pale blue, and the contrast closed in on my mind like the ever-deepening twilight.

We watched the trickle. I knew the door was solid enough — a mass of four hundred pounds of steel — and I knew the inward pressure would increase with every foot of depth. So I gave the signal to descend quickly. After that, the flashlight was turned on the doorsill a dozen times during our descent, but the stream did not increase.

Two minutes more and "four hundred feet" was called out; 500 and 600 feet passed overhead, then 700 feet, where we remained for a while.

Ever since the beginnings of human history when first the Phoenicians dared to sail the open sea, thousands upon thousands of human beings had reached the depth at which we were now suspended and had passed on to lower levels. But all of these were dead, drowned victims of war, tempest, or other Acts of God. We were the first living men to look out at the strange illumination — and it was of an indefinable translucent blue quite unlike anything I have ever seen in the upper world, and it excited our optic nerves in a most confusing manner. We kept thinking and calling it brilliant, and again and again I picked up a book to read the type, only to find that I could not tell the difference between a blank page and a colored plate. I brought all my logic to bear, I put out of mind the excitement of our position in watery space and tried to think sanely of comparative color, and I failed utterly. I flashed on the searchlight, which seemed the yellowest thing I had ever seen, and let it soak into my eyes, yet the moment it was switched off it was like the long vanished sunlight — it was as though it never had been — and the blueness of the blue, both outside and inside our sphere, seemed to pass materially through the eyes into our very beings. This is all very unscientific, quite worthy of being jeered at by optician or physicist, but there it was. I was excited by the fishes that I was seeing perhaps more than I have ever been by other organisms, but it was only an intensification of my surface and laboratory interest; I have seen strange fluorescence and ultra-violet illumination in the laboratories of physicists; I recall the weird effects of color sifting through distant snow crystals on the high Himalayas; and I have been impressed by the eerie illumination, or lack of it, during a full eclipse of the sun; but this was beyond and outside all or any of these. I think we both experienced a wholly new kind of mental reception of color impression. I felt I was dealing with something too different to be classified in usual terms.

All our remarks were recorded by Miss Hollister, and when I read them later, the repetition of our insistence upon the brilliance, which yet was not brilliance, was almost absurd. Yet I find that I must continue to write about it, if only to prove how utterly inadequate language is to translate vividly feeling and sensation under a condition as unique as submersion at this depth.

The electric searchlight now became visible. Heretofore we could see no change whatever in the outside water when it was turned on, but now a pale shaft of yellow — intensely yellow — light shot through the blue, very faint but serving to illuminate anything which crossed it. Most of the time I chose to have it cut off, for I wanted more than anything else to see all that I could of the luminescence of the living creatures.

After a few minutes I sent up an order, and I knew that we were again sinking. The twilight (the word had become absurd, but I could coin no other) deepened, but we still spoke of its brilliance. It seemed to me that it must be like the last terrific upflare of a flame before it is quenched. I found we were both expecting at any moment to have it blown out, and to enter a zone of absolute darkness. But only by shutting my eyes and opening them again could I realize the terrible *slowness* of the change from dark blue to blacker blue. On the earth at night in moonlight I can always imagine the yellow of sunshine, the scarlet of invisible blossoms, but here, when the searchlight was off, yellow and orange and red were unthinkable. The blue which filled all space admitted no thought of other colors.

We spoke very seldom now. Barton examined the dripping floor, took the temperatures, watched and adjusted the oxygen tank, and now and then asked, "What depth now?" "Yes, we're all right." "No, the leak's not increasing." "It's as brilliant as ever."

And we both knew it was not as brilliant as ever, but our eyes kept telling us to say so. It actually seemed to me to have a brilliance and intensity which the sunshine lacked — sunshine, that is, as I remembered it in what seemed ages ago.

"Eight hundred feet" now came down the wire and I called a halt There seemed no reason why we should not go on to a thousand; the leak was no worse, our palm-leaf fan kept the oxygen circulat ing so that we had no sense of stuffiness, and yet some hunch — some mental warning which I have had at half a dozen critical times in my life — spelled *bottom* for this trip. This settled, I concentrated on the window for five minutes.

The three exciting internal events which marked this first trip were, first, the discovery of the slight leak through the door at 300 feet, which lessened as we went down; next, the sudden short-circuiting of the electric light switch, with attendant splutterings and sparks, which was soon remedied. The third was absurd, for it was only Barton pulling out his palm-leaf fan from between the wall of the sphere and the wire lining of the chemical rack. I was wholly absorbed at the time in watching some small fish, when the sudden shrieking rasp in the confines of our tiny cell gave me all the reactions which we might imagine from the simultaneous caving in of both windows and door! After that, out of regard for each other's nerves, we squirmed about and carried on our various duties silently.

Coming up to the surface and through it was like hitting a hard ceiling — I unconsciously ducked, ready for the impact, but there followed only a slather of foam and bubbles, and the rest was sky.

We reached the deck again just one hour after our start and sat quietly while the middle bolt was slowly unscrewed. We could hear our compressed air hissing outward through the threads until finally the bolt popped off and our eardrums vibrated very slightly. After a piece of boiler-factory pounding the big door finally swung off. I started to follow and suddenly realized how the human body could be completely subordinated to the mind. For a full hour I had sat in almost the same position with no thought either of comfort or discomfort, and now I had severally to untwist my feet and legs and bring them to life. The sweater which was to have served as cushion I found reposing on one of the chemical racks, while I had sat on the hard cold steel in a good-sized puddle of greasy water. I also bore the distinct imprint of a monkey wrench for several days. I followed Barton out on deck into the glaring sunshine, whose yellowness can never hereafter be as wonderful as blue can be.

While still upside down, creeping painfully, sea-lionwise over the protruding circle of bolts, I fancied that I heard a strange, inexplicable ringing in my ears. When I stood up, I found it was the screeching whistles on the boilers and the deeper-toned siren of the *Gladisfen* giving us, all to ourselves, a little celebration in mid-ocean. The wind was right and my staff on Nonsuch ten miles away saw the escaping steam through the telescope-binoculars, later heard the sound faintly, and knew that we had made our dive and ascent in safety.

Four days later we were able to put to sea again, and sent the bathysphere down empty to 2000 feet. By the judicious use of white lead we had effectively stopped the leak in the door, and there was no tangle or twist of hose. A tiny flaw which we had watched with suspicion on the outer rim of one of the quartz windows had not increased. The only novelty in the way of unexpected happenings after this two hours' submergence was that about three feet of the hose had been forced inside the sphere. When this was rectified, Barton and I climbed inside and started enthusiastically for a deeper plunge. Everything went well until at 150 feet we began to experience bad static on the phone. A sentence would come through clearly and then only a mixture of spluttered words. It improved for a while, but at 250 feet Barton said, "My God! The phone is broken." It was a tragic exclamation, and I felt exactly as he did. The leak on our other trip, the short-circuiting, the static today — these were all annoying but not terrifying, and, as I have already mentioned, the sound of the human voice had, all unconsciously to us, seemed a much surer bond than the steel cable or the sturdiness of the sphere. We had neither of us felt before quite the same realization of our position in space as we did now. It seemed as if hose, cable, and all had gone. We had become veritable plankton. I visualized us as hanging in mid-water for as long as the Flying Dutchman roamed the surface above. The silence was oppressive and ominous, and our whispers to each other did nothing to alleviate it. The greenish blue outside became cold and inimical. We did our best to signal with the searchlight, knowing that answering flickering must be reflected in the checking bulb on deck. We felt a sudden weight beneath us and knew that we were being reeled swiftly to the surface. A momentary delay came as the single clamp was removed. Some part of my brain worked steadily on and counted twenty-four jellyfish swimming past, and then we rose swiftly. As soon as the ascent first began, my mind went to the people on deck, and I knew that they were getting the worst of this dive. As we shot into the air and over the bulwarks, I caught a glimpse of our assistants' faces and those of the crew, and I knew how little we had appreciated the strain of the last two minutes. I jammed my face as close to the glass as possible and assumed what I supposed was a reassuring grin, and the second attempt at a deep dive was over. A broken wire had caused the trouble, and eventually we had to cut off and throw away fifty fathoms of hose.

The next day, June 11, was a perfect one for our work, and we were able to take advantage of it and make the deepest descent of this season, to a depth of 1426 feet, or well over a quarter of a land mile. When we went out in our launch to the *Ready*, we found there had been a fire on board in the night which had taken several hours to put out. The side and part of the aft gunwale had been badly charred, but no serious damage done, while the hose, winch, and sphere had escaped. With our ancient barge looking a little more than usual like a deserted hulk, we put to sea again. As there was a current and an outward set, this time I stopped at a point in the ocean five miles south of Nonsuch, where former soundings had given us a depth of 750 fathoms.

This was Dive Number Seven for the bathysphere, and we climbed in at 9:50 A.M. We had made a number of improvements since the first dive. The inside had been painted black so as not to interfere with observations. Barton had come to look upon his very greasy leather skull-cap as a mascot, so when he could not find it, the central bolt was unscrewed and the *Ready* searched thoroughly for five minutes, after which he found he was sitting on it. We now had a special place for fans and monkey wrenches, and I arranged a shelf for my notebook and pencil, specimens of scarlet crustaceans, and a book with type and plates to test the pseudo brilliance of the light. The cushion was in its right place, and we had built a shield to shut out the lateral glare from the searchlight. We had also learned to cover the *chevaux-de-frise* of bolts at the entrance with sacking, and so to soften the effects of our frantic wrigglings in and out. The shackle of the cable had been shifted from the central to the posterior hole so that the sphere tipped slightly forward and downward when swinging free. This gave me a better outlook in a slightly oblique, downward direction. The hose fastening on the sphere had been tightened so that there was less chance of our being smothered in its entering, entwining coils, which would have been an undramatic, Laocoön ending.

This time we took a chance on everything being in good order, and did not make an experimental submergence. We fastened the Tropical Research house flag of the New York Zoological Society and that of the Explorers' Club to the bathysphere, and tied a very ancient squid wrapped in cheesecloth just beneath the observation windows. Dangling in front and just to one side was a cluster of luminous hooks attractively baited. With the searchlight ready to turn on, I felt that I had contrived all the enticements possible for luring deep-sea fish within my observational zone.

Barton and I were screwed down and bolted in at ten o'clock, and four minutes later touched water. The surface was crossed with small wavelets, and three times before we were completely submerged the distant *Gladisfen* and the level horizon were etched clearly on the glass, and as instantly erased by a green and white smother. We sank slowly and I peered upward and watched the under side of the surface rise above me. When the rush of silvery bubble-smoke imprisoned beneath the sphere had passed, the surface showed clear. From the point of view of a submarine creature, I should by rights call it the floor of the air, and not the ceiling of the water. Even when diving in the helmet, I am always conscious of the falsity of calling the water wet when I am once immersed in it. Spray blows in one's face and leaves it wet, but down below, the imprisoned air sailing upward slips through one's fingers like balloon pearls; dry, mobile beauty, leaving only a pleasant sensation.

And now I looked up at our vertical wake of thousands of iridescent swimming bits of air, and, for a moment, forgot whither we were bound.

The boundary of air and water above me appeared perfectly solid and like a slowly waving pale-green canopy, quilted everywhere with deep, pale puckers — the sharp apexes of the wavelets above showing as smooth, rounded indentations below. The sunlight sifted down in long, oblique rays as if through some unearthly, beautiful cathedral window. The host of motes of dust had their exact counterpart in mid-water, only the general feeling of color was cool green, not yellow. The water was so clear that I could see dimly the distant keel of the *Gladisfen*, rolling gently. And here and there, like bunches of mistletoe hanging from a chandelier, were clusters of golden sargassum weed, with only their upper tips hidden, breaking through into the air. A stray berry went past my window, and I saw an amusing likeness between its diminutive air-filled sphere and that which was at present my home.

The last thing in focus, of the upper world, was a long, undulating sea serpent of a rope dangling down from the side of the *Ready*.

We had asked to be lowered slowly. When less than 50 feet beneath the surface, I happened to glance at a large deep-sea prawn which I had taken for color experiment. To my astonishment it was no longer scarlet, but a deep velvety black. I opened my copy of *Depths of the Ocean* and the plate of bright-red shrimps was dark as night. No wonder I thought of the light as cool.

On this and other dives I carefully studied the changing colors, oth by direct observation and by means of the spectroscope. Just beneath the surface the red diminished to one half its normal width. At 20 feet there was only a thread of red, and at 50 the orange was dominant. This in turn vanished at 150 feet, and 300 feet found the whole spectrum dimmed, the yellow almost gone and the blue appreciably narrowed. At 350 I should give as a rough summary of the spectrum 50 per cent blue-violet, 25 per cent green, and an equal amount of colorless pale light. At 450 feet no blue remained, only violet, and green too faint for naming. At 800 feet there was nothing visible but a narrow line of pale grayish-white in the green-blue area, due, of course, to the small amount of light reaching my eye. Yet when I looked outside, I saw only the deepest, blackest blue imaginable. On every dive this unearthly color brought excitement to our eyes and minds.

A few familiar *Aurelia* jellyfish drifted past while we were sinking to 50 feet, and at 100 feet a cloud of brown thimble jellies vibrated by the window. These were identical with those which we had observed in vast swarms in Haiti.* They are supposed to be surface forms, but here they were pushing against my window 20 fathoms down. They were the first organisms which showed that the fused quartz did away with all distortion. Full 20 feet away I could see them coming, and the knowledge of their actual size — that of a thimble — gave me a gauge of comparison which helped in estimating distance, size, and speed of unknown organisms.

I found that little things could change my whole mental outlook in the bathysphere. Up to this moment I had been watching the surface or seeing surface organisms, and I had focused so intensely upward that what was beneath had not yet become vivid. As the last thimble jelly passed, an air bubble broke loose from some hidden corner of the sphere, and writhing from the impetus of its wrenching free, rose swiftly, breaking into three just overhead, and the trio vanished. Now I felt the isolation and the awe which increased with the dimming of the light; the bubble seemed the last link with my upper world, and I wondered whether any of the

* *Beneath Tropic Seas*, Linuche jellies, pp. 20–23.

watchers saw it coming, silver at first, then clothing itself in orange and red iridescence as it reached the surface — to break and merge and be lost forever.

At 200 feet there occurred my first real deep-sea experience on this dive, something which could never be duplicated on the surface of the water. A six-inch fish suddenly appeared, nosed the bag of ancient squid, and then took up its position close to the glass of my window, less than a foot away from my face. Something about it seemed familiar, yet it was strange. In size, shape, and general pattern it was very like a pilot fish, *Naucrates ductor*. Twice it swam back to the delectable bait and three times returned to where it almost diametered my circular outlook. Then I knew what the trouble was — it was the ghost of a pilot fish, pure white with eight wide, black, upright bands. At 200 feet a pilot fish could not be the color he is at the surface, and, like Einstein's half-sized world, here was a case where only the faulty, transient memory of man sealed up in a steel sphere had any right to assert that under different conditions the fish would show any colors other than the dark upright bands. I am certain that the fish itself aided this pale appearance, for it has considerable power of color change, but this was very different from the mere expansion and contraction of dermal chromatophores. At 250 feet I saw the pilot fish going *upward*.

There was a similarity between two- and three-hundred-foot levels in that most of the fish seen were carangids, such as pilot fish and *Psenes* (this has no human or Christian name, but its technical one is so interesting to pronounce that this can be excused!). Long strings of siphonophores drifted past, lovely as the finest lace, and schools of jellyfish throbbed on their directionless but energetic road through life. Small vibrating motes passed in clouds, wholly mysterious until I could focus exactly and knew them for pteropods, or flying snails, each of which lived within a delicate tissue shell and flew through life with a pair of flapping, fleshy wings.

At 400 feet there came into view the first real deep-sea fish — cyclostomes, or roundmouths, lantern fish, and bronze eels. The former meant nothing at first; I took them for dark-colored worms or shrimps. Only when I saw them at greater depths in the search-light, did I recognize them. Of all the many thousands of these fish which I have netted, I never saw one alive until now. The lantern fish (myctophids) came close to the glass and were easy to call by name. Instead of having only a half dozen scales left, like those caught in the nets, these fish were ablaze with their full armor of iridescence. Twice I caught the flash of their light organs, but only for an instant. An absurdly small and rotund puffer appeared, quite out of place at this depth, but, with much more reason, he probably thought the same of me.

Big silvery bronze eels came nosing about the bait, although what they expected to accomplish with their exceedingly slender and delicate jaws is hard to imagine. Their transparent larva also appeared, swimming by itself, a waving sheet of watery tissue. Pale shrimps drifted by, their transparency almost removing them from vision. Now and then came a flash as from an opal, probably the strange flat crustacean well named *Sapphirina*. Ghosts of pilot fish swam into view again at this level.

Here, at 400 feet, we found that we could just read ordinary print with an effort, and yet to the unfocused eye the illumination seemed very brilliant. I found that the two hours' difference between 10 A.M. and noon, marking the two dives, Numbers Four and Seven, although both were made in full sunlight, resulted in 50 per cent less illumination at 10 A.M. than at noon.

At 500 feet I had fleeting glimpses of fish nearly two feet long, perhaps surface forms, and here for the first time I saw strange, ghostly, dark forms hovering in the distance — forms which never came nearer, but reappeared at deeper, darker depths. Flying snails passed in companies of fifty or more, looking like brown bubbles. I had seen them alive in the net hauls, but here they were at home in thousands. As they perished from old age or accident or what not, their shells drifted slowly to the bottom, a mile and a half down, and several times when my net had accidentally touched bottom it had brought up quarts of the empty, tinkling shells.

Small ordinary-looking squids balanced in mid-water. I hoped to see some of the larger ones, those with orange bull's-eye lights at the tips of their arms, or the ones which glow with blue, yellow, and red light organs. None came close enough, however, or it may be I must wait until I can descend a mile, and still live, before I can come to their haunts.

A four-inch fish came into view and nosed the baited hook. It was almost transparent, the vertebrae and body organs being plainly visible, the eyes and the food-filled stomach the only opaque parts. Since making the dive, I have twice captured this fish, the pinkish semitransparent young of the scarlet big-eyed snapper.

At 550 feet I found the temperature inside the bell was seventy-six degrees, twelve degrees lower than on deck. Near here a big leptocephalus undulated past, a pale ribbon of transparent gelatin with only the two iridescent eyes to indicate its arrival. As it moved, I could see the outline faintly — ten inches long at least — and as it passed close, even the parted jaws were visible. This was the larva of some great sea eel.

As 600 feet came and passed, I saw flashes of light in the distance and at once turned on the searchlight, but although the blue outside seemed dark, yet the electric glare had no visible effect, and we turned it off. The sparks of light and the distant flashes kept on

from time to time, showing the power of these animal illumina-
tions.

A pale-blue fish appeared, yet the blue of the pilot fish does not
exist at this depth. Several *Seriola*-like forms nosed toward me.
They must have drifted down from the surface waters into these
great pressures without injury. Dark jellyfish twice came to my eyes,
and the silvery eels again. The flying snails looked dull gold, and I
saw my first shrimps with minute but very distinct portholes where
the lights must be. Again a great cloud of a body moved in the
distance — this time pale, much lighter than the water. How I
longed for a single near view, or telescopic eyes which could pierce
the murk. I felt as if some astonishing discovery lay just beyond
the power of my eyes.

At another hundred feet a dozen fish passed the sphere swimming almost straight upright, yet they were not unduly elongate
like the trumpet fish which occasionally assume this position in
shallow waters near shore. I had only a flash of the biggest fish yet
— dark, with long tapering tail and quite a foot in length. Shrimps
and snails drifted past like flakes of unheard-of storms. Also a large
transparent jellyfish bumped against the glass, its stomach filled
with a glowing mass of luminous food.

Here and at 800 feet a human being was permitted for the first
time the sight of living silver hatchet fish, heliographing their silver
sides. I made Barton look out quickly so he could verify the unexpected sight.

Here is an excerpt, of a very full seventeen minutes, direct from
the transcription which Miss Hollister took of my notes telephoned
up from 800 feet on Dive Number Eleven:

> *June 19, 1930, 1:24 P.M., depth 800 feet: 2 black fish 8 inches
> long going by, rat tailed, probably* Idiacanthus; *2
> long, silver, eellike fish, probably* Serrivomer (*fish and inverte-*

brates go up and down the shaft of light like insects); 3 *mycto-phids with headlights*, Diaphus (*work with a mirror next time*); 2 *more different myctophids; the same* 3 *myctophids with headlights;* 20 *pteropods and* 6 *or* 8 Argyropelecus *to-gether;* 3 *more pteropods* (*little twinkling lights in the dis-tance all the time, pale greenish in color*); *eels,* 1 *dark and* 1 *light;* big Argyropelecus *coming, looks like a worm head on;* Eustomias-*like fish* 5 *inches long;* 30 *cyclostomes, grayish white.*

We had left the deck at ten o'clock, and it was twenty-five minutes later that we again reached our record floor — 800 feet. This time I had no hunch — reasonable or unreasonable — and three minutes later we were passing through a mist of crustaceans and flapping snails at 900 feet. We both agreed that the light was quite bright enough to read by, and then we tried pica type and found that our eyes showed nothing definite whatever. With the utmost straining I could just distinguish a plate of figures from a page of type. Again the word "brilliant" slipped wholly free of its usual meaning, and we looked up from our effort to see a real deep-sea eel undulating close to the glass — a slender-jawed *Serrivomer*, bronzy red as I knew it in the dimly remembered upper world, but here black and white.

At 1000 feet we had a moment's excitement when a loop of black sea-serpenty hose swung around before us, a jet-black line against blackish blue.

Almost at once the sparks we had seen higher up became more abundant and larger. At 1050 feet I saw a series of luminous col-ored dots moving along slowly, or jerking unsteadily past, similar and yet independent. I turned on the searchlight and found it effective at last. At 600 feet it could not be distinguished; here it cut a swath almost material across my field of vision, and for the first time, as far as I know, in the history of scientific inquiry, the life of these depths was visible. The searing beams revealed my colored lights to be a school of silver hatchet fish, *Argyropelecus*, from a half to two inches in length and gleaming like tinsel. The marvel of the searchlight was that up to its sharp-cut border the blue-blackness revealed nothing but the lights of the fish. In this species these burned steadily, and each showed a colorful swath directed downward — the little iridescent channels of glowing reflections beneath the source of the actual light. These jerked and jogged along until they reached the sharp-edged border line of the searchlight's beam, and as they entered it, every light was quenched, at least to my vision, and they showed as spots of shining silver, revealing every detail of fin and eye and utterly absurd outline. When I switched off the electricity or the fish moved out of its path, their pyrotechnics again rushed into visibility. The only effect of the yellow rays was to deflect the path of each fish slightly away from its course. Like active little rays of light entering a new medium, the argyros passed into the searchlight at right angles to my eye and left it headed slightly away. With them was a mist of jerking pteropods with their delicate shields, frisking in and out among the hatchet fish like a pack of dogs around the mounts.

My hand turned the switch and I looked out into a world of inky blueness where constellations formed and reformed and passed without ceasing. At this moment I heard Miss Hollister's voice faintly seeping through Barton's headphone, and it seemed as if the sun-drenched deck of the *Ready* must surely be hundreds of miles away.

I used the searchlight intermittently, and by waiting until I saw some striking illumination, I could suddenly turn it on and catch sight of the author before it dashed away.

At 1100 feet we surveyed our sphere carefully. There was no evidence of the hose coming inside, the door was dry as a bone, the oxygen tanks were working well, and by occasional use of our palm-leaf fans the air was kept sweet. The walls of the bathysphere were dripping with moisture, probably sweating from the heat of our bodies condensing on the cold steel. The chemicals were working well, and we had a grand shifting of legs and feet, and settled down for what was ahead of us.

In the darkness of these levels I had not been able to see the actual forms of the hatchet fish, yet a glance out of the window now showed distinctly several rat-tailed macrouridlike fish twisting around the bend of the hose. They were distinct and were wholly new to me. Their profiles were of no macrourid I had ever seen. As I watched, from the sides of at least two there flashed six or more dull greenish lights, and the effect on my eyes was such that the fish vanished as if dissolved into water, and the searchlight showed not a trace. I have no idea of what they were.

At 1200 feet there dashed into the searchlight, without any previous hint of illumination, what I identified as *Idiacanthus*, or golden-tailed serpent dragon, a long, slender, eellike form which twisted and turned about in the glare, excited by some form of emotion. Twice it touched the edge and turned back as if in a hollow cylinder of light. I saw it when at last it left, and I could see no hint of its own light, although it possesses at least three hundred light organs. The great advantage of the electric light was that even transparent fins — as in the present case — reflected a sheen and were momentarily visible.

From this point on I tied a handkerchief about my face just below the eyes, thus shunting my breath downward and keeping the glass clear, for I was watching with every available rod and cone of both eyes what was going on outside the six-inch circle of the quartz.

At 1250 feet several more of the silver hatchets passed, going

upward, and shrimps became abundant. Between this depth and
1300 feet not a light nor an organism was seen: it was 50 feet of
terrible emptiness, with the blue mostly of some wholly new color
term — a term quite absent from any human language. It was
probably sheer imagination, but the characteristic most vivid was
its transparency. As I looked out, I never thought of feet or yards
of visibility, but of the hundreds of miles of this color stretching
over so much of the world. And with this I shall try to leave color
alone for a space.

Life again became evident around 1300 feet and mostly luminous. After watching a dozen or more fireflylike flashes, I turned
on the searchlight and saw nothing whatever. These sparks, brilliant though they were, were kindled into conflagration and
quenched in the same instant upon invisible bodies. Whatever
made them was too small to reach my eyes, as was almost the host
of copepods, or tiny crustaceans, through which we passed now
and then. At one time I kept the electric light going for a full
minute while we were descending, and I distinctly observed two
zones of abundance and a wide interval of very scanty motelike
life. When they were very close to the glass, I could clearly make
out the jerking movements of copepods, but they were too small
to show anything more. The milky *Sagitta*, or arrowworms, were
more easily detected, the eye catching their swift dart and then
focusing on their quiet forms. While still near 1300 feet a group
of eight large shrimps passed, showing an indeterminate coloration.
We never took large shrimps at these comparatively shallow levels
in the trawling nets.

Barton had just read the thermometer as seventy-two degrees
when I dragged him over to the window to see two more hatchet
fish and what I had at last recognized as roundmouths. These are
the most abundant of deep-sea fish, and we take them in our nets

by the thousand. Flickering forms had been bothering me for some time, giving out no light that I could detect, and twisting and wriggling more than any shrimp should be able to do. Just as my eyes had at first refused to recognize pteropods by their right names, I now knew that several times in the last few hundred feet I had seen cyclostomes, or roundmouths. In the searchlight they invariably headed uplight, so that only their thin-lipped mouths and tiny eyes were turned toward me.

Before Barton went back to his instruments, three squids shot into the light, out, and in again, changing from black to barred to white as they moved. They showed no luminescence.

At 10:44 we were sitting in absolute silence, our faces reflecting a faint bluish sheen. I became conscious of the pulse throb in my temples and remember that I kept time to it with my fingers on the cold damp steel of the window ledge. I shifted the handkerchief on my face and carefully wiped the glass, and at this moment we felt the sphere check in its course — we felt ourselves press slightly more heavily on the floor, and the telephone said, "Fourteen hundred feet." I had the feeling of a few more meters' descent, and then we swung quietly at our lowest floor, over a quarter of a mile beneath the surface.

I pressed my face against the glass and looked upward, and in the slight segment which I could manage I saw a faint paling of the blue. I peered down, and again I felt the old longing to go further, although it looked like the black pit mouth of hell itself — yet still showed blue. I thought I saw a new fish flapping close to the sphere, but it proved to be the waving edge of the Explorers' Club flag — black as jet at this depth.

My window was clear as crystal, in fact clearer, for, as I have said before and want to emphasize, fused quartz is one of the most transparent of all substances and transmits all wave lengths of sunlight. The outside world I now saw through it was, however, a solid blue-black world, one which seemed born of a single vibration — blue, blue, forever and forever blue.

Once, in a tropical jungle, I had a mighty tree felled. Indians and convicts worked for many days before its downfall was accomplished, and after the cloud of branches, leaves, and dust had settled, a small white moth fluttered up from the very heart of the wreckage. As I looked out of my window now, I saw a tiny semitransparent jellyfish throbbing slowly past. I had seen numerous jellyfish during my descent, and this one aroused only a mental note that this particular species was found at a greater depth than I expected. Barton's voice was droning out something, and when it was repeated, I found that he had casually informed me that on every square inch of glass on my window there was a pressure of slightly more than six hundred and fifty pounds. The little moth flying unharmed from the terrific tangle and the jellyfish drifting gently past seemed to have something in common. After this I breathed rather more gently in front of my window and wiped the glass with a softer touch, having in mind the nine tons of pressure on its outer surface!

However, it was not until I had ascended that the further information was vouchsafed me that the pressure of the water upon the bathysphere from all directions at our greatest depth was more than six and a half million pounds, or, more concisely, 3366.2 tons. So, far from bringing about an anticlimax of worry, this meant hardly more than the statement that the spiral nebula in Andromeda is 900,000 light years away. Nevertheless, I am rather glad that this bit of information was withheld until I had returned to the surface. If I had known it at the time, I think the two tenths of a ton might have distracted my attention — that four hundred pounds being fraught with rather a last-straw-on-the-camel's-back significance!

Like making oneself speak of earthrise instead of sunset, there was nothing but continued mental reassertion which made the pressure believable. A six-inch dragonfish, or *Stomias*, passed — lights first visible, then three seconds of searchlight for identification, then lights alone — and there seemed no reason why we should not swing the door open and swim out. The baited hooks waved to and fro, the edge of one of the flags flapped idly, and I had to call upon all my imagination to realize that instant, unthinkably instant, death would result from the least fracture of glass or collapse of metal. There was no possible chance of being drowned, for the first few drops would have shot through flesh and bone like steel bullets.

The duration of all this rather maudlin comment and unnecessary philosophizing occupied possibly ten seconds of the time we spent at 1426 feet.

When, at any time in our earthly life, we come to a moment or place of tremendous interest, it often happens that we realize the full significance only after it is all over. In the present instance the opposite was true, and this very fact makes any vivid record of feelings and emotions a very difficult thing. At the very deepest point we reached I deliberately took stock of the interior of the bathysphere: I was curled up in a ball on the cold damp steel, Barton's voice relayed my observations and assurances of our safety, a fan swished back and forth through the air, and the ticking of my wrist watch came as a strange sound of another world.

Soon after this there came a moment which stands out clearly, unpunctuated by any word of ours, with no fish or other creature visible outside. I sat crouched with mouth and nose wrapped in a handkerchief and my forehead pressed close to the cold glass — that transparent bit of old earth which so sturdily held back nine tons of water from my face. There came to me at that instant a tremendous wave of emotion, a real appreciation of what was momentarily almost superhuman, cosmic, of the whole situation: our barge slowly rolling high overhead in the blazing sunlight, like the merest chip in the midst of ocean, the long cobweb of cable leading down through the spectrum to our lonely sphere, where, sealed tight, two conscious human beings sat and peered into the abyssal darkness as we dangled in mid-water, isolated as a lost planet in outermost space. Here, under a pressure which, if loosened, in a fraction of a second would make amorphous tissue of our bodies, breathing our own homemade atmosphere, sending a few comforting words chasing up and down a string of hose — here I was privileged to peer out and actually see the creatures which had evolved in the blackness of a blue midnight which, since the ocean was born, had known no following day; here I was privileged to sit and try to crystallize what I observed through inadequate eyes and to interpret with a mind wholly unequal to the task. To the ever-recurring question, "How did it feel?" I can only quote the words of Herbert Spencer: I felt like "an infinitesimal atom floating in illimitable space." No wonder my sole written contribution to science and literature at the time was, "Am writing at a depth of a quarter of a mile. A luminous fish is outside the window."

The return trip was made in forty-three minutes, an average of one foot every two seconds. Twice during the ascent I was aware of one or more indefinite large bodies moving about at a distance. On the way down I had accredited them to an over-excited imagination, but after having the experience repeated on several deep dives, I am sure that I did see shadowy shapes of large and very real living creatures. What they were I can only guess, and live in hopes of seeing them closer on some future descent.

We had ascended to 1000 feet when Miss Hollister sent down word that a gull was flying about the *Ready,* and a moment later

said that it was a young herring gull. I relayed the information that
I had made a note of it — qualifying thus as the first ornithologist
who had ever made a submarine bird note, and then contradicted
it by remembering that when diving in a helmet off Marlborough
in the Galápagos, I had recorded on my zinc tablet a passing visit
from two penguins.

Immediately after, to a question as to what was happening, I
retorted that two *Ipnops* had taken our hooks — this fish being
one that we much desired but had not yet seen or caught. Down
came the statement that one of the men had just scooped up a big
deep-sea fish with his hands on the surface. I jeered — and then,
seeing a luminous fish, snapped into an excited account of what
began to come into view. When we returned to the surface, I was
astonished to discover that the capture of the deep-sea fish was not
a rather pointless joke but a fact. In some way a giant specimen of
the lantern fish, *Myctophum affine*, had got mixed up with the
sphere or hose and had come to the surface somewhat damaged.
Once disabled, it had *fallen up*, as is the horrible fate of deep-sea
fish in trouble. It was the world's record for size.

We stepped out of the bathysphere at 11:52 after a submergence of almost two hours, with good air to breathe, perfect tele-
phonic communication, and the memory of living scenes in a world
as strange as that of Mars.

I have never doubted the success of the adventure as a whole,
but I had much less faith in the possibility of seeing many living
creatures from the windows in the bathysphere. The constant
swaying movement due to the rolling of the barge high overhead,
the great, glaring white sphere itself looming up through the blue
murk, the apparent scarcity of organisms at best in the depths of
the ocean as revealed by our net hauls, and finally the small size of
the aperture, hardly as large as one's face — all these seemed

handicaps too severe to be overcome. Yet the hope of such observations was the sole object of the entire project. We never
thought of it as a stunt, as beating the record of anyone, as the-
first-white-man-who-had-ever . . .

This secret skepticism made the actual results all the more satisfying. As fish after fish swam into my restricted line of vision —
fish which heretofore I had seen only dead and in my nets — as I
saw their colors and their absence of colors, their activities and
modes of swimming and clear evidence of their sociability or solitary habits, I felt that all the trouble and cost and risk were repaid
many fold. For two years I had been studying the deep-sea fish in
a limited area of mid-ocean off Nonsuch, and now when we were
at the bottom of our pendulum, I realized that I, myself, was down
where many hundreds of nets had been hauled. During the coming
year I should be able to appreciate the plankton and fish hauls as
never before. After these dives were past, when I came again to
examine the deep-sea treasures in my nets, I would feel as an astron-
omer might who looks through his telescope after having rocketed
to Mars and back, or like a paleontologist who could suddenly an-
nihilate time and see his fossils alive.

CHAPTER 6
Contour Diving

THE four final bathysphere dives of 1930 were devoted to what I might describe as contour diving, to steal part of an aviation term. This is decidedly more risky than deep dives in the open sea, but is of equal scientific importance. It opens up an entirely new field of possibilities: the opportunity of tracing the change from shallow-water fauna, corals, fish and so forth, to those of mid-water, with the hope finally of observing the disappearance of the latter, and the change, gradual or abrupt, into the benthic, or deep-sea, forms of life. We know absolutely nothing of this at present, as the transition zone is so rough and untrawlable that there is no method known of learning anything about it. Nets are torn to shreds and dredges catch almost at once; the wire breaks and not a single organism comes up.

I worked out the simplest method during the last dives of 1930. I brought the *Gladisfen* and *Ready* as close to shore as I dared on a day of perfect calm with a slight offshore wind and there began diving, with the bottom, nine or ten fathoms down, actually in sight from the deck. We were lowered to within two fathoms of the reefs while the *Ready* drifted slowly seaward. As it turned out, the first two dives were probably the most foolhardy things we could have done, for the sphere drifted backward, and from my window I could see only the bottom over which we had passed. If our projecting wooden landing gear had caught in a sudden rise of reef, it would have gone very hard with us. As it was, I could only flatten my eyes against the quartz and try to adapt my elevation orders to what the contour promised. Once a crag passed two feet beneath us, and I had a most unpleasant moment while we were rushed up 30 feet.

Early on the following day, June 20, Barton affixed a double wooden rudder of boards to orient the sphere, so that in our subsequent contour dives we swung around and faced forward. Another improvement was the shifting of the shackle to the posterior hole, so that the whole apparatus tilted slightly downwards in front. I had the lead heaved constantly and telephoned to me, and so rapidly were my orders transmitted to the man at the winch that we rose and fell swiftly as we progressed slowly seaward, now ordering a fathom or two of elevation to escape a projecting coral crag, then dropping down into a submarine valley until the bottom again became visible. In spite of a constant watch ahead, accidents were on several occasions barely avoided.

Two years later, in 1932, when we were diving from the deck of a large tug, one of the contour dives was marked by the narrowest escape which we ever experienced. We had already hurdled two low coral reefs twenty and thirty feet high. A group of large fish held our attention directly below. I could not quite identify them, and they were whirling around some focus of attraction when a dark shadow fell across the window. I looked up and saw that we were drifting rapidly toward an enormous crag, or part of a coral reef, towering fifty feet or more above us and covered on its almost perpendicular slope with great outreaching crags and sharp, water-worn hooks and snags. I sent the most urgent S.O.S. on the wire to haul us up as rapidly as possible, and we could almost hear the hissing steam as the winch began to turn at full speed. Fortunately there were no clamps to cut free. As we ascended, we swung nearer and nearer the cliff, and the waving sea fans and great anemones grew larger, and we were so close that every detail, every small fish became visible.

I fully expected to strike and had already formulated the next order, which would have been to let us out as rapidly as we had been drawn up and to go astern full speed. In this way we might have slipped down the reef without becoming entangled, and when the tug had backed over the reef, we would have swung clear.

But again the clarity of the fused-quartz windows deceived us, and we just cleared the summit, passing so close to it that I am sure our wooden base must have brushed the fingerlike plumes on the reef top.

Even if we had struck, no harm might have resulted; we might have bumped and scraped up and over the top. But a straight blow on one of the quartz windows, or getting badly tangled in one of those steel-hard, outreaching crags would not have been so good.

On the other side I had us lowered 65 feet, as the bottom sloped rather steeply, and when we were again within a few feet of the bottom, I saw below us a wide beach of white sand mixed with water-worn pebbles and shells and sloping against the outer base of the great reef. I could even see ripple marks and could distinguish the various kinds of shells. This was to me one of the most interesting discoveries of all my dives. It was undoubtedly the old foreshore of Bermuda, the ancient beach which was above water at the last glacial period, say twenty-five thousand years ago. At that time there was so much ice locked up on the continents that the oceans were 250 feet lower than they are at present, and the dry-land area of Bermuda was then doubtless measured in hundreds instead of tens of miles. Not far beyond this beach of olden time an abrupt and awful drop led down in a bluish-black abyss, where the bottom was lost and could not be recovered without too much risk.

Visibility was usually excellent, except close inshore and for a few days after a severe storm or hurricane when cloudiness put an end to the work. When the water was clear, I could make out and identify all coral and algal growths and fish down to two inches in length. After several years' work in the diving helmet I was familiar with the Bermuda fauna down to six and eight fathoms, and now the thing which impressed me most as I went deeper was the increased size of the fish — snappers, grunts, angelfish and chubs, trumpet fish, surgeons, parrots and jacks — all were as large or larger than I had ever seen them when diving in shallower water near shore. Now and then a fish was seen larger than any of its kind ever taken in Bermuda, and this in spite of the fact that angling is carried on down to ninety fathoms.

Certain species of mid-water fish offered unexpected problems. The two most abundant were the blue chromis, *Demoisellea cyaneus*, and the smooth sardine, *Sardinella anchovia*. The former holds a place on the Bermuda list solely on the basis of a single doubtful record of seventy years ago, while there are few published records of this sardine. Yet on these shallow dives I saw school after school of each, hundreds of chromis swimming loosely, and tens of thousands of sardines in dense formations. When the latter sighted the bathysphere, they turned downward as one fish and poured past like elongated, silvery raindrops. The chromis usually passed on a horizontal plane. In the West Indies recently I saw these two species in vast numbers about the shallowest reefs near shore.

Once I saw an interesting exchange of courtesy, one which I

have observed many times when diving near shore. The giant cerulean parrot fish browse on hard coral as a horse tears off mouthfuls of grass. After an interval of feeding, when the teeth and jaws and scales of the head are covered with debris, the fish upends in midwater and holds itself motionless while a school of passing wrasse, all tiny in comparison with the big fish, rush from all sides and begin a systematic cleaning of the large fish's head. As in most relationships between different species of animals, this is founded on mutual benefit, the parrot fish getting a free cleaning, and the wrasse finding a supply of particles of food ready at hand.

On the very last dive of 1930, we were 30 feet down, with the bottom at least a hundred feet beneath, when, without the slightest warning, the green water rained blue parrot fish. They were all deep cerulean blue (*Scarus caeruleus*), almost unmarked, and they varied from about six inches to four feet. Hundreds and hundreds streamed obliquely past and downward, unending lines of vivid blue, and they extended far beyond my vision in every direction. Some were the merest shadow ghosts of parrot fish in the distance; others almost brushed the glass; and the downpour did not cease — we merely passed through it. It seemed as if all the parrot fish of Bermuda had suddenly decided to leave for the depths of the open sea.

Once before, a few miles to the westward, when I descended on a particularly rough day in my helmet to a depth of 30 feet, I saw a similar migration or gathering of the blue parrot fish clans. On this occasion they were filled with curiosity about me and milled about for five minutes, fairly blanketing me — almost obliterating the surrounding seascape.

Well out from shore on one of these contour dives I had the thrill of suddenly seeing a thin, endless sea serpent. We were drifting slowly along, lifting over a toothed ridge or settling down into a valley of caverns and gorges, when, without warning, I saw a long black line undulating over the bottom, clearly visible when over a bed of sand, or vanishing behind a mass of giant sea plumes. A second glance revealed it as the deep-sea transatlantic cable resting quietly on its bed and carrying innumerable messages of hope and fear, joy and death. Kipling's words took on a new significance, and I shall never send a cable again without this memory, nor shall I ever forget the breath-taking belief of the first few seconds.

Another important phase of this method of observation is the physical geography of the bottom. I have been able to describe and map over a mile of bottom, seen from five to twenty feet elevation while I was traversing steadily seaward. After we passed the great loop of the cable, all visible life ceased, and we drifted over a wide expanse of desert, with no fish or plumes or living coral. I have no idea of the significance of this dead zone.

I have never succeeded in following the bottom lower than 350 feet. Increasing cloudiness of the water and greater obscurity have made it impossible to distinguish anything, and the danger of getting hung up and snapped off on some projecting cliff is too constant to progress blindly.

With a calm sea, a steady offshore breeze or current, and our searchlight in working order it will be possible sometime to make a systematic survey of the Bermudian insular shelf. Even to repeat the conditions under which we worked would mean perfect facility for recognizing the change in species of fish and such invertebrates as echinoderms and horny corals, to see and name and note the bottom limits of algae and brain coral, and, finally, to watch for the end of water-worn and air-worn rocks and the beginnings of the lava flows of old Bermuda Mountain.

II
Pacific Cruise

CHAPTER 7
Albatrosses

ON the third day out from San Diego, March 28, at eight o'clock in the morning, a pair of black-footed albatrosses appeared and followed us all day.

The fireside adventurer in the world's literature knows the albatross from that swinging rhythm which I have quoted before:

> And a good south wind sprung up behind;
> The Albatross did follow,
> And every day, for food or play,
> Came to the mariners' hollo!

The common people read in their daily rag of an albatross which nearly killed the robber of its nest, and when it was finally overcome and slain, it was found to have a wingspread of twenty feet. The ocean-going tourist has a happy memory for the rest of his life when a shearwater or a fulmar, if not indeed a booby, is pointed out to him as the famous bird. Seamen on lonely seas watch the birds day after day with unintelligent and often superstitious attention but with complete satisfaction at having something to relieve the vastness and eternal sameness of water.

The most recent authority on this group of birds begins his

monograph with the sentence, "Our information about the habits of albatrosses is fragmentary and sketchy."

There are a few characteristics which set apart this small family of sea birds. Of slight scientific import, but of immense popular interest, is size. The wandering albatross is unquestionably the greatest of all fliers of the sea. Exaggerations of the truth in this respect still persist, like the useless and harmful appendix, in the best of human associations. The latest edition of the *Encyclopaedia Britannica* keeps alive the record of a spread of wing of seventeen feet. The final word of accuracy seems to be Dr. Robert Cushman Murphy's statement:

> I conclude that a wing-spread of about eleven and a half feet, with the wings of a dead bird stretched out as tightly as possible, represents the maximum expanse of any known bird on the earth. The twelve-foot albatross needs verification; the thirteen-foot albatross is probably a myth.

As to weight, seventeen pounds seems the greatest accurate record, with a possibility of individuals reaching nineteen.

These figures do not make albatrosses the largest of flying birds, for condors, swans, wild turkeys, and great bustards challenge them in weight as well as in actual square area of flight surface. But for speed, control, and sheer grace albatrosses have no equal in the air.

If the above-mentioned reader of exaggerated newspaper accounts could have been off northwest Africa some fifty or sixty millions of years ago, his desire for records and notorious statements could have been abundantly satisfied, for a distant ancestor of the albatross living somewhere about that place and time may have spread his pinions to an extent of five and twenty feet. Again, if this well-named fossil bird were living on the earth today, the put-upon ocean tourist need not be ashamed of mistaking a shearwater for an albatross, for this great bird of old was something of a connecting link between albatrosses, petrels, pelicans, and frigate birds.

Even living albatrosses resemble each other so much in their various plumages that a minute inspection of the beak is the surest way of differentiating between certain species. Another important point in telling which is which on the wing is the ocean, or the particular part of the ocean, in which any one bird is observed. No stranger habit exists in the world of birds than the relationship between the breeding and the distribution areas of albatrosses. If we imagine that our American bald eagle wandered throughout part of the year over all of the North American continent, from Alaska and Labrador to Florida and Panama, and that at the nesting season every bald eagle in existence flew straight toward New York City and built its nest and reared its young in an area of one quarter of Central Park equal to a square of ten city blocks, we can the better visualize the corresponding life of albatrosses. The sooty albatross, for example, wanders over the whole South Atlantic and Indian oceans, reaching to Australia on the east and to the bitter limits of Antarctic pack ice a thousand miles south of Cape Horn. At the call of the breeding season all the adult sooty albatrosses, hundreds and thousands of them, head for the tiny islets of Gough and Tristan da Cunha far out in the southern Atlantic. On certain limited areas of these specks of dry land they all nest and incubate.

The feats of actual flight exhibited by albatrosses are almost beyond the possibility of exaggeration. Dr. Murphy has sifted the true from the questionable and records that a single individual bird has been known to follow a definite ship for three thousand miles. A wandering albatross tagged at its nest was captured three years later six thousand miles away. As to speed, a maximum of one hundred miles an hour is admitted as truth.

One strange thing about albatrosses sets them apart from all their petrel relations — an inexplicable dance between friends. As far as we know, these birds are essentially monogamous, indulging in a well-marked courtship, the individuals of mated pairs being devoted to one another, sharing both nest building and the long tedious period of incubation and care of the single chick.

Years ago on the breeding grounds of the Galápagos albatross I watched and filmed another type of dance, or ritual, or give-it-your-own-name, which seems to be quite peculiar to albatrosses. This is an elaborate performance of posturing and fencing with slight vocal accompaniment. I have seen it indulged in by an incubating pair, by one of this same pair and two separate outsiders, by two birds casually meeting, and by a bird which, in the course of a long and difficult progression through the rookery, met and successively performed with three birds one after the other. And I have induced a bird to go part way through the performance by bowing myself. It is reported to be indulged in well after the proper breeding season, hence is nonsexual in time as well as in partners, more or less indiscriminate, and quite apart from the more conventional courtship of the usually accepted definition. It awaits explanation, which cannot help being of the greatest interest.

The real courtship is no rough-and-tumble affair as with the house sparrow, nor purely a vocal performance such as that of the house wren. Nor is it an eternally repeated statuesque posture as exhibited by the golden pheasant. It combines all these with added expressions of passion and devotion which are almost human in variety and complexity. Dr. L. H. Matthews of the *Discovery* expedition has written a most fascinating account of all this, a few paragraphs of which are well worth salvaging from his scientific report on the "Birds of South Georgia." Concerning the wandering albatross he writes:

In courting before pairing several males gather around one female and bow to her, bringing the head down close to the ground. As they do this they utter a harsh groaning sound, and the female bows and groans back at them. After several bows the males open the wings to about half their extent and side-step around her. They then edge into a position so that they are directly facing her and open the wings to their widest extent so that the tips of the primaries are raised above the level of the head and are curved forwards toward the female. At the same time the males raise the head so that the bill points straight up into the sky, and give vent to a loud braying cry. They then close the wings and start all over again. Several males do this at the same time around the one female, but they do not all act in unison so that unless they are watched carefully one gets the impression of half a dozen male birds dancing around the female and going through a series of haphazard actions, but one finds that they all adhere to the same course of action, if attention is directed to each in turn.

After pairing has taken place and before incubation has started, the courtship ceremonies are even more elaborate than before. The nests are built on the bases of those of the last season, which are now trodden to about half their full size. The female sits on the half-built nest and the male walks around among the surrounding tussocks picking up bits of peaty moss and mud. He brings these to the female and deposits them on the edge of the nest and bows to her, at the same time making a groaning sound. She returns the bow and groan to him and then takes up the load of material which he has brought and arranges it on the nest, shuffling around on half-bended legs to stamp it down with her large webbed feet. The male then sits down on the ground close alongside the nest and makes a vibrating bubbling noise in the throat several times, at the end of each call stretching the head up and braying with the bill open. The female answers him, and then they start nibbling the feathers of each other's throats, heads, and necks. This is followed by a further round of bubbling and braying and then the male gets up and goes to fetch another load of nest-building materials.

After every four or five loads that the male brings to the nest both sexes go through a more passionate demonstration of affection. The male brings his load and deposits it, and after bubbling and braying, and nibbling each other's heads and necks, they both stand up, and the female steps down off the nest. Facing each other, they both stretch up their heads and give a harsh bray with the bill widely open. Immediately after the bray the bill is brought so that it points vertically downwards and is thrust among the plumage of the breast. The bray is expiratory, and a lower, inspiratory note is made while the bill is touching the breast. They then lean forward together and touch the tips of each other's bills. After this they both keep the neck bent forwards, and bend the head upwards slightly and vibrate the mandibles very rapidly, causing a peculiar rattling sound. The syrinx is not used in producing this sound, which has a slight musical ring, rising from a low note to a high one during its performance. This is owing to the increasing quickness of the vibrations and to the filling of the lungs with air during the process so that the thorax acts as a sound-box.

After these antics are repeated several times the male starts to walk sideways around the female, working his head from side to side with each step, and the female steps around without moving her position so that she is facing him all the time. The male spreads his wings widely, and pointing his head upwards repeats the vibration of the mandibles. He next bends forward, doing it again, and the female answers him, at the same time spreading her wings too. They continue in this attitude, stretching out and touching bills, then vibrating and touching their own breasts with the tip of the bill, twenty times or more, after which pairing takes place and they return to the nest, the female sitting down on it and the male carry-ing on his work of collecting material for it.

I have quoted this in detail because its strangeness and mystery typify so thoroughly our abounding ignorance concerning these and numbers of other living creatures. Albatrosses may be considered as merely gigantic storm petrels and count among their relations many other oceanic birds. Yet among none of the others do we find anything like this complex courtship and the still more inexplicable dance which goes on long after the seasons of courtship and incubation.

The black-footed albatross which we saw from the *Zaca* is so called from a translation of its technical title, *Diomedea nigripes,* which, to the observer from the deck of a vessel, is about as enlightening as would be the information given when walking down Fifth Avenue that the passing crowd were white-footed Americans. This albatross is one of the dark species, and the plumage on the whole is a delicate sooty brown, slightly paler on the neck and lower parts. A conspicuous field mark is the white area on the forehead and around the bill together with a small white spot behind the eye. The black-footed albatross is considerably smaller than the wandering albatross, with a correspondingly less extent of wings. But it is all albatross as regards its infinite grace and power of flight, its wide range and restricted breeding area, and its strange dance ritual.

It wanders from Japan to Alaska over all the North Pacific and from the Aleutian Islands and Bering Sea south to the equator. It nests on a few small islets northwest of Hawaii. Here the birds focus from all directions at the breeding season, court and dance, lay eggs, incubate, rear young, and still dance on and on. Dr. Fisher, writing of the albatrosses of Laysan Island, says:

If we wander over the island on a moonlight night a strange scene greets us. Nocturnal petrels and shearwaters are wide-awake and are sobbing and yowling as if all the cats in a great city had tuned up at once. Back and forth in the weird light flutter shadowy forms, and from beneath our feet dozing young gonies bite at us in protest. Down by the lagoon where the herbage is short we can see for some distance and the ghostly forms of the albatrosses shine out on all sides, busily bowing and fencing, while the nasal sounds of revelry are borne to us from far across the placid lagoon, and we know that in other parts of the island the good work is still progressing. And so in the leisure moments of the long summer days, and far into the night, these pleasure-loving creatures seem to dance for the joy of dancing.

On a late March day, as I have said, a pair of these birds followed us all day long. For some time after they apeared in the distance, I paid little attention to them, deceived by their shearwaterlike flight and the lack of any scale to show their relative size. But the first time they approached a group of gulls their great spread and larger bodies marked them at once for what they were, and my glasses showed all their principal characters. A quartet of herring gulls also kept with the *Zaca* all day and frequently alighted close together in our wake among the flotsam of galley refuse. One of the albatrosses would then soar up, bank sharply, put on all its brakes of wings, tail and feet, and settle, scattering all the gulls.

The beat of these albatrosses was a slow and irregular circling of the *Zaca*. Coleridge showed himself a reliable ornithologist when he wrote:

> *It ate the food it ne'er had eat,*
> *And round and round it flew.*

The flight was low, usually close to the surface, following the course of the swells. If the albatrosses' exact flight could have been plotted, it would be irregularly wavy, reflecting the succession of swells and occasional cross waves which rose and fell like malleable mounds beneath them. Their course was never in a straight line, but more like the method of a shearwater, a slow swinging to right and left, ending often in a sharp bank, the tip of the down wing sometimes touching and seeming to press against the surface. A number of times during the morning they alighted on the water well off to one side, fed on some bit of sea food, and took off again with much greater ease than could a cormorant or duck under the same conditions.

On another day four albatrosses and the same number of small black storm petrels kept us company. I watched one of the former slither down into the water off our starboard quarter within a landing space of not more than six feet. As it alighted, I could clearly distinguish the white rump and upper tail coverts which proclaimed it a bird of the year in not fully adult plumage. It picked up a dead squid, gulped it down, and shook its beak several times in the water. Then in the face of a very slight breeze it spread its wings, took off with exactly two paddles of its great webbed feet, and rose easily.

For an hour or two around midday the albatrosses disappeared entirely, but at two o'clock, when we were on deck after lunch, a bird came up rapidly from behind. Crocker took a chance on a long shot; the bird shook itself but was apparently unhurt, although it soon alighted on the water. A second albatross now appeared and soared twice over the sitting bird and vanished. The *Zaca* made a quick revolution on its course. As we approached, the bird rose without difficulty and started off, but turned about almost at once and flew directly toward us. A second shot, well within range, killed it instantly. Again we steered toward it and gathered it up in a hand net as we passed. It was almost in full plumage, weighed six pounds, and had a spread of wings of exactly seven feet.

In the early afternoon this incident was repeated in almost every detail. Both proved to be females, showing no hint of an approaching breeding season. While one had eaten a large number of short stems of seaweed forming a good-sized wad in the stomach, the other had swallowed forty squids, some of which must originally have been of large size.

Superstitiously inclined readers may be interested to know that an hour after we had shot the second albatross we lowered three deep-sea nets to three, four, and five hundred fathoms respectively where the chart showed a depth of twelve hundred. When the wire was reeled in, it was quite devoid of nets, rings, and bridles, having evidently landed upon, scraped along, and torn away on some uncharted rock elevation less than three hundred fathoms below the surface.

> "God save thee, ancient Mariner!
> From the fiends, that plague thee thus! —
> Why look'st thou so?" "With my cross-bow
> I shot the Albatross."

But, you see, the mariner shot for pleasure, and the only use made of his *Diomedea exulans* was to have it, unpleasantly enough, hung about his neck, while we examined, described, measured, compared, skinned, and preserved, as well as recorded food, parasites, and all the minutiae which go toward a better understanding of the What? Why? and How? of an albatross!

CHAPTER 8

Flight Patterns

THE flight of birds is as characteristic as the walk of individual human beings. We can often recognize a friend by his mode of walking at a distance greater than we could know him from stature or features. But flight is of far deeper significance than human progression, being a trenchant character in the distinction of families and even species. To approximate this significance, we would have to suppose among human beings that all Germans, men, women, and children, progressed only by means of the goose step, or all Hottentots went through life solely by hops, skips, and jumps.

I have sometimes been doubted when I have identified a bird by a momentary flash of its wings as it shot past, but even the brief glimpse of migrants crossing the face of the full moon is sufficient to tell warbler from goldfinch or swallow from woodpecker. It would be unthinkable, to our minds, for a hummingbird to soar or a duck to progress by long, dipping loops, yet during our week in Inez Bay I twice observed a flight phenomenon almost as strange and fully as unexpected.

One of the commonest sights from dawn to dusk was the great numbers of cormorants and pelicans. There were thousands of the

former and scores of the latter. As in Magdalena Bay the cormorants passed to and from distant fishing grounds in long straight
skeins, sometimes several hundred in a single line, each close behind the bird in front until an oblique view often showed a solid,
continuous line of dark bodies. Ducklike, their wings beat in swift
constant measure, a steady unvarying vibration, with, however, no
attempt at synchronization with the bird in front or behind.

The flight of the brown pelicans was radically different from that
of the cormorants, and in all parts of the world where these great
ungainly birds are found their flight, to the least detail, is as identical as that of a bird and its shadow. Their favorite formation is in
short lines, straight or oblique, consisting usually of about six to
twenty individuals, although fewer and more are common sights.
The moment the birds leave their roosting places on rocky islets or
low bushes, or when, satiated with their catch of fish, they start
for home, they fall into single file, and at once the leader sets a
rhythm which they all follow. The only way I can indicate this in
words is flap-flap-flap-gliiiiiiiiiide, flap-flap-flap-flap-flap-gliiiiiiiiiiiiide.
There may be five or seven or even a dozen flaps, while the length
of the glide seems dependent on the amount of impetus. With a
head wind there will be more flaps and a shorter glide. Before any
appreciable slowing down or loss of elevation there ensues another
series of flaps. If, en route, a new bird joins the file, he instantly
falls into step, or, rather, flap.

The imitative reaction to the leader by the others appears almost
instantaneous, especially in the case of a half dozen pelicans, but
in a line of twenty or thirty a slight individual delay is apparent.
This mental drag is multiplied by each bird in succession, becoming so appreciable that there may be two nodes of wing-flapping
down the line, just as the delay in sound-carrying of a military band
may, to the eye of the observer as he looks down the distant col-

umns, make successive segments of a long parade seem to be out of step.

The fact of this drag in the flight of pelicans shows conclusively that the tempo and change is taken by each bird in turn from the one in front and not from the leader. The position of this leader is, I believe, sheer accident, and although he must bear the brunt of the full force of any head wind, I have never seen him fall back or change places.

In addition to this regular lock-step flight, pelicans, in spite of their apparent ungainliness, can set their half-closed wings and their beaks in the form of an arrowhead, and dive with terrific speed and effectiveness. Still more surprisingly they can soar quite as well as vultures or eagles. I shall never forget a first visit to Florida with John Burroughs when our glasses resolved a cloud of slowly revolving motes high in the heavens over Indian River into several hundred brown pelicans.

But this is aside from the intention of this present theme. One day in a moment of relaxation I was looking idly from the deck of the *Zaca* out over the waters of Inez Bay. A file of a dozen pelicans passed and a distant line of cormorants, recorded automatically by some part of my mind but not disturbing my meditation. Another small flock of birds aproached and my eye wandered idly to it with the instant effect of a strong electric shock. I stood up and knocked over my chair. I instinctively reached for my glasses but did not lift them for the birds were only fifty yards away. The arresting thing was that of the six birds three were pelicans and three cormorants, all head to tail, close together in perfect alignment in the order of pelican, pelican, cormorant, cormorant, pelican, cormorant.

This was strange enough, although these birds associate in most friendly fashion both in their roosting places and when fishing, but the fact which had aroused all my concentrated interest was that the cormorants had *gone pelican* in their flight. In spite of the disparity in size these six birds were all flap-flap-flap-flap-gliiiding as if all were pelicans.

To the unornithologically minded this may seem a fact of but slight importance, but to me it was fraught with significance. Throughout all the days, years, and no-one-knows-how-many centuries and millenniums these pelicans had slowly evolved their physical characters together with their specialized flight, and the latter had always seemed to me as unvarying and specific as the voicelessness or the great beak and pouch; on the other hand, the swift, unchanging beat of cormorants' wings appeared inseparable from the emerald eye, strong hooked beak, and mobile neck. Yet here, for no apparent reason, three cormorants had enlisted in the lock-step squad of brown pelicans and were flapping and gliding as if from the time of the fossil nth great-grandparents of all cormorants they had never flown otherwise. It gave to think furiously and brought the flight of all birds into a renewed appraisal and interest.

This aroused watchfulness was rewarded within a week when several of us were sorting a dredge haul and my observation was confirmed, this time with the emphasis of simplicity in that only two birds were concerned. A single pelican came along, closely followed head to tail by a single cormorant, and from the time when we first saw them abeam to when they passed beyond the range of our glasses they never ceased to keep perfect pelican rhythm, flap-flap-flap-flap-gliiiiiiiiiide.

Pelicans and cormorants, together with four other diverse groups — the gannets, frigates, tropic birds, and snakebirds — form six families of a single order, *Pelecaniformes*, but the individuality in action of them all when on the wing is almost as great as their physical disparity. Twice I have seen a booby and a pelican closely teamed in swift flight, but this is not as surprising as the other association, for both boobies and pelicans have the same make-and-break sequence of progress.

The way of the frigates, or man-o'-war birds, in the air is a slow wonderful flapping with wings so long, so narrow, so angular, and under such perfect control that we often forget the narrow body and seem to be looking at an avian caduceus, pure alar harmony. Indeed, slow-motion pictures show that the wings may sometimes present actual independence of movement, one pinion acting as a brake while the other controls impetus in a spiral descent.

The shift in flight pattern from cormorant to pelican is remarkable for several reasons: first, from the specific point of view, the relinquishing of an age-old, evolved method of flight for even the temporary adoption of another, more specialized; second, the heavy, compact, anserine body of the cormorants would seem ill adapted to the long glide so close to the surface of the water; third, the adoption, even rarely, of the pelicans' flight hints that there is a very real advantage in the single-line formation with its strung, temporal beads of flap and glide — perhaps as windbreak and in

Flight rhythm of pelicans, of cormorants, and of the
two when flying together

reduction of air resistance. And while we may say with some assurance that the intermittent glide is a conservation of energy, an instant response is to wonder why the pelicans and boobies alone require this economy.

CHAPTER 9
Whale-Sharking

EXCEPT when we went after game fish in the launch, all our work at sea in the vicinity of Cape San Lucas and the banks was carried on from the deck of the *Zaca* itself, but there came a day toward the end of our stay in these waters when we entered more intimately into the life of the ocean. For days we had been seeing very large fins of sharks, placed far apart, cutting the surface here and there. We had put them down as giant blue sharks or hammerheads, or perhaps marlin larger than any that had ever been caught.

On the second day of May, when we had pulled up the last dredge on Arena and were headed south toward Gorda, we once again sighted an immense fin, off the port bow, with a second fin so far behind that it seemed as if two or even three sharks must intervene. It must be realized that it is exceedingly difficult to judge the size of an object isolated at sea, as there is nothing with which to compare it, but in this case there was no doubt of the extraordinary size of the fin.

The *Zaca* held on her course, but the wandering fins gained, finally turned toward us, and passed close. I happened to be some distance up the ratlines, and as I looked down, I saw the water suddenly filled with a pattern of multitudinous white spots: a single giant whale shark, largest of all living fish and one of the rarest of sharks, was swimming slowly past.

The fish was visible until we lowered the launch and started out. For ten minutes thereafter no sign was seen of him, then the fins appeared a hundred yards away and we headed toward them at full speed. Ben was at the engine and Frank and Pemasa had a great harpoon fastened by a long rope to an empty gasoline drum.

When we came alongside, the fish was only about three feet below the surface. We waited until he was almost awash, when both men made a beautiful pole-vaulting dive, with the harpoon between them. They struck hard and then leaped into the air and let their whole weight bear down, driving the harpoon home. At the same moment I fired a revolver straight down into the creature's head, making at least two direct hits. The drum was thrown overboard and vanished.

After fifteen minutes, excited yells came from the crew on the yacht. They directed our attention to the farther side, and there, three hundred yards away, was the float. We found it completely crumpled in the middle like a huge hourglass, evidence of the pressure at the great depth to which it must have been dragged. It was moving slowly and steadily along. We soon caught up with it and for the next hour had the excitement of our lives. The great shark was never more than fifteen feet down and usually was swimming within a yard of the surface.

Twice we returned to the yacht for additional harpoons, but in spite of the greatest efforts of the Samoans, the instruments bent as if they had struck steel. Pe said this often happened in the case of large sharks of more common species. The first harpoon enters easily, but after that some sort of tightening of the dermal muscles makes it impossible to drive through. We tried to slip a cable over the drum and around the tail, but the speed, slow though it was, prevented us. I watched the shark for an hour or more, trying to memorize the spots and patterns.

There seemed to be no end in sight, for we had no harpoon gun, and we were only helpless midgets in our inability to do further harm to this giant. His steady progress seemed to indicate that he could go on like this for days and weeks. Finally we tightened the noose around the drum and led the cable back to the *Zaca*, where it was made fast; whereupon the whale shark headed readily alongside. But the moment he felt the pull of the yacht he tore out the harpoon as if it had been a pin and was off, without any undue haste, for the open Pacific. I estimated his length at thirty-five feet, but the splendid photographs which John Tee-Van took from the crosstrees permitted direct comparison with the known length of the launch and proved the shark to be forty-two feet from head to tail tip.

We found in this fisherman's paradise that these sharks were actually common, and the Japanese captain of a tuna boat told me that he often saw ten in a day. This abundance is seen in its true importance when we recall that only eighty or eighty-five individual whale sharks have ever been recorded in the annals of science.

This man was well informed, and thoughtful and conservative in all his replies to my questions. He had been tuna fishing throughout seven seasons and had almost never gone out from San Lucas on one or more days' fishing without sighting a whale shark. The first may appear in March but more usually in early April, and the last sharks are seen in September or, rarely, early October. No one knows where they go, and no young ones have ever been seen. Arena and Gorda seem to be the center of distribution, and the captain had never noticed them beyond La Paz up the gulf or Turtle Bay on the west coast of the peninsula.

The largest he had ever seen was at least two fathoms longer than his tuna boat, which measured fifty-five feet. The smallest was not less than three or four fathoms. They never attack, but are very troublesome when, by accident, they get entangled in the fish nets. This man had seen them as far west in the Pacific as Nagoya, off southern Japan. The Japanese call them *babā*, meaning "old woman," because they appear to have no teeth. The tuna fishermen dislike steaming through these waters at night because of the danger of running into a whale shark and losing a propeller or a rudder from a single flick of the gigantic tail.

We counted ten distant whale sharks during the course of the three days following our first identification. Sometimes we sighted the same individual several times, and in four or five cases we could recognize a shark seen an hour or a day before by some unusual visible character. One had the first dorsal irregularly scooped out behind; another had both fins notched at the tips; and one which we followed and photographed for two hours had, as a recognizable brand, a two-inch hole straight through the tail fin near the tip.

On the third of May, John Tee-Van, Jocelyn Crane, and I followed this last specimen for two hours, most of the time just overhead or close alongside. By racing our engines suddenly, we were able to disturb him just sufficiently to make him turn slightly to one side or the other, and were thus able to herd him into patches of slick calm where we could photograph and observe as through clear air. We watched shark suckers, some more than two feet in length, slither over his great body, their favorite place being near the base of the pectoral fins. Several months later I took this whole series of photographs to the British Museum of Natural History, where they were of use in helping with the construction of a whale-shark model, and later the same thing occurred in our American Museum in New York.

The upper half of the pectoral fins and the whole head from these fins forward were very thickly covered with two-inch white, or creamy-white, spots in dense, irregular order. From here aft the spots became abruptly larger and farther apart, in regular rows separated by white vertical lines, as far as the second dorsal fin, where they gradually disappeared. There was no sign of the horizontal white lines which are usually accredited to the pattern of this shark, nor of more than one lateral dermal ridge. From every aspect the entire surface appeared perfectly smooth. The head was exceedingly blunt and broad, with a mouth fully six feet across. The teeth in the huge maw (as I knew from examination of a museum specimen) were arranged in great sheets consisting of thousands upon thousands of denticles, each about an eighth of an inch in length. The tail fin was enormous and swept regularly back and forth like some part of a mighty engine, its tip swinging from one side to the other in three seconds through a space of ten feet.

The strangest thing about the whole apparition was the result of the identity of the shark's general background color with that of the sea water. Whenever we first came within sight of one of these beings, the outline was so indistinct that, as I have already said, the effect was of the water being suddenly filled with a vast number of unconnected, drifting spots of white.

The five great gills showed not the slightest movement. They were slightly open and remained so. The lower portion of the last gill opening was distended, and opened and closed regularly all the time. This characteristic recalled an identical condition in the nurse shark, a shark of similar activity and general habits which perhaps needs only the functioning of part of the last gill to allow a sufficient flow of water over the gills.

The first record of a whale shark seen by man was of a fifteen-foot specimen in the waters of Table Bay, Cape of Good Hope, on an April day one hundred and eight years ago. Some fishermen harpooned this white-spotted shark and towed it ashore, where fortunately it came into the possession of a scientist, Dr. Andrew Smith, who dissected it, gave it a name, and twenty years later published in full a very complete account together with a hand-colored illustration.

Since then less than a hundred others have been reported from various parts of the world. The greatest number have been seen near the Philippines, while the second area of abundance is off this western coast of Mexico. Sixty-five feet seems to be an authentic estimate of the largest, which puts it well at the head of all the fish in the world for actual length and body weight.

It has much in common with the nurse shark as regards gentleness and inoffensiveness. While it is almost without fear, yet even after being harpooned, it has never been known to attack or turn on man or boat. With a harpoon deep within its body it swims or dives deliberately, making haste but slowly, and dying quietly.

Its thousands of minute teeth, arranged filewise around its jaws, function only in hindering the escape of more active small fish. The method of feeding is apparently to swim slowly along the surface, as our fish were doing, and to strain out through its gills the slower-swimming shrimp and fish, together with the host of lesser floating life. It is perhaps significant that the other dominant form of oceanic creatures with identical feeding habits — the whalebone whales — also challenges and exceeds this great shark in size. In connection with its blind method of feeding we find the eyes small, as being of little use, the mouth enormous and placed at the very front of the head somewhat like the opening of a trawling net, the gills developed into deep horny sieves, and the teeth reduced to minute denticles.

The courtship of the whale shark, if any, its mating, migrations, and its young are all mysteries. We do not know whether the young are hatched from eggs or are born alive. Dr. Gudger, who has spent many years in researches on these creatures, considers the latter method as almost certain.

After we had seen the last of our harpooned shark, in the final dredge drawn up from the Lucas banks I found four *Amphioxus* — inchling relics of the very origin of fish life on our planet. A few hours before, we were struggling impotently with at least eight tons of the most specialized shark living today. A greater contrast would be difficult to imagine.

CHAPTER 10

Clarion: The Lonely Isle

FOUR hundred miles southwest of Cape San Lucas the bottom of the Pacific pushes abruptly up through two miles of black, inky depths into the warm sunlight, and on for another thousand feet. This bit of dry land, measuring two by six miles, is known as Clarion Island. We had chosen it for our third and last focus of exploration and study. I had greatly desired to visit a Pacific oceanic island in order to compare the general conditions existing there with those of Bermuda in the Atlantic. Clarion fulfilled every requirement.

Whatever place I am studying always becomes an individual of sorts, or rather possessed of some small special spirit whose influence is everywhere apparent. Inez Bay was a gentle, friendly, feminine personality whom we woke from sleep, but so quietly that she watched us with tolerant, pleased, half-closed eyes as we went about our work. She secreted nothing, held nothing back, making us feel that only the limitations of our senses prevented our solution of all her mysteries. She even held her breath so that nothing should cloud the face of the watery window, wide open to our human eyes. If we had stayed on, we should have come perilously near to taking all her kindness for granted, expecting such favors as due our investigations in the name of science.

San Lucas presented a mixture of characters, all moderate, fraternal, leaving us to our own devices, not especially interested, absorbed in their own occupations, but evincing a definite guardian spirit. After writing this, I realized that unconsciously I had defined the dignified cluster of Gray Friars, imagining apposite characteristics of Los Frailes.

Clarion, as we shall see, was to us a lonely hermit, a flagellant, cruel to himself and, while devoid of animus, offering nothing of help or kindness to any intruder. Whatever we learned or accomplished was an "in-spite-of."

The island, together with three sister specks several hundreds of miles away, is known as the Archipelago of Revillagigedo, which, when a Mexican says it, becomes a soft whisper of a name, full of charm. The pronunciation of this word is a worthy dinner-table addition to the names of two Mexican volcanoes, Po·po·ca·te'petl and Ix·ta·ci'huatl. It goes thus: Ruh-véeya-hee-gáy-do.

On the tenth of May the *Zaca* came within sight of Clarion and anchored at the entrance of an open bay on the south shore. It is a strange thing to come to an island like this, or to any place on earth wholly new to us, and even before we have put foot on shore, while we are still looking at major landmarks and features that come to the eye at first sight, to know that all these which now are surprises will, after a week's time, become memories, and memories which may crop up throughout the rest of our life, unexpectedly and at incongruous moments. That red headland would, at the end of a week, vanish forever into the faintest of faint mists against the southern horizon. Yet, for no reason at all, it will re-create itself in my memory on some most casual occasion, or when I am threatened with death.

My first impression, looking toward the west, as Clarion came in sight, was of high precipitous cliffs, strata sloping at oblique angles, much dark red and less gray. The profile of the island was of high rounded summits, with slopes covered with pale greenish vegetation. There was very little exposed rock; the soft grassy growth covered everything.

On the south side at Sulphur Bay, which we approached slowly, the cliffs were less high and more even, ending in two long curved beaches with more low, black lava cliffs beyond. White dots massed here and there resolved in the glass into colonies of boobies. As we neared the shore, frigate birds, boobies both brown and white, and a few tropic birds soared overhead. A dozen pairs of mating turtles were scattered about in the water. Thus far the tropic birds were the only reminder of Bermuda, Clarion's mountainous character and lack of all human occupation emphasizing this difference. But our later comparisons were to be concerned with less conspicuous and more significant phenomena.

The moment we began preparations for landing we realized the amazing individuality of this island. It came near being an absolute no man's land, for there was only one short extent of shore in the entire circumference, possibly fifty yards in width, where it was possible for a boat to land. We piled into the dory, were towed by the launch to the outermost swell, and turned loose. Frank, the Samoan, took the oars, headed for a bit of sandy beach bounded by great black boulders, and watching his chance, drove in on a curving green swell which broke just in front and carried us headlong amid froth and bubbles, and we jumped out into two feet of backwash. Only in this narrow lane was the full strength of the encircling waves of Clarion broken. Close on each side great breakers roared past us. Eight or ten feet high they were, with crests blowing back like the manes of white horses.

The island is guarded on every side by this never-ceasing pounding of waters, and very few human beings have ever set foot upon it. So isolated is Clarion that many of the creatures which call it home are distinct from all their relatives living in other parts of the world. On our first walk we saw four species of birds, a snake, and a lizard which are peculiar to this two-by-six speck in mid-ocean.

The girdle of crashing waves exerts very important effects on the animal life of the shore. Large coat-of-mail shells and limpets are the only mollusks which can withstand the eternal pounding, for every movable stone has been cast high up on the terraced beaches, and sheltering cracks and crevices are few. Only the great, scarlet *Grapsus* crabs, the Sally lightfoots, can slither with impunity over the rocks, clinging fast with their eight stout legs. Even the tide pools are not free from the beating breakers, and the fishes which find them safe are few in number.

The lava foreshore with its scattered black boulders vividly recalled the littoral of Galápagos. Beyond this a terrace of broken coral and shells rose steeply to the very edge of a welter of morning-glories and palmate cactus. And now we saw how wrong we were when we thought we saw the slopes covered with soft grass. For hundreds of yards the cactus formed so solid a carpet that not a step could be taken inland. And often when the long soft stems of the grass seemed to afford easy walking, we learned to our cost that it was only a thin covering for more cactus.

The first of the great sandy beaches we named at sight Turtle Beach, for many trails led up from the water and across its wide expanse, each looking like the track of a miniature armored tank. They led directly to patches of disturbed sand with which later on I was to become intimately acquainted. Looking seaward beneath the great, green onrushing waves, I detected what I thought were four large lava rocks on the bottom. A second glance showed them to be turtles waiting for nightfall before creeping ashore. No crash of water could injure their solid armor.

The first reptile I saw was a medium-sized snake, earthen brown in color, on the lava rocks near the water. I caught it without trouble. Farther on a coot lay dead on the coral, a storm-blown waif, the first of its kind ever recorded from Clarion. Nine ravens came down from the nearest hills, looked at us, croaked dismally, and flew off.

Next a brown wrenlike, yet warblerlike bird flew up from the beach and sang a short zizzing song with a catch in it, more like that of a warbler than a wren. This, however, was the brown Clarion wren, living here and nowhere else in the world. A dove flushed from our path and a turquoise lizard appeared and vanished in the same second of time; both were natives and peculiar to Clarion.

All of them recalled nearly related species which we had seen in Mexico and Lower California, but their separateness seemed to me far more trenchant than any variation in color or size. It made real the centuries upon centuries of isolation, the months and years marked on Clarion not by any human calendars but by the indistinct seasons, the regular and thousand times repeated time of breeding and nesting of every creature, and the unseen, unrecorded eons of storms and sunshine, days and nights.

As we walked along the upper level of the beach, well above the reach of storm waves, we came across traces of small booby colonies, the ground-nesting, blue-faced ones. Many of the nests were already deserted, having served their use. All of them were merely separate, bare, rounded patches with white guano radiating in every direction. The radiating effect is due to the instinctive effort of the sitting bird to keep the nest as clean as possible. In each of these localities were a very few birds still on their nests, incubating one or two or, in one case, three eggs; still more rarely a booby was found sitting on newly hatched chicks. They were all late nesters, having suffered some accident to their first eggs or young, and were quite fearless, just as I had seen them in the Galápagos years ago. We had to push them, snapping and biting, off their nests to inspect the eggs. Often, on following days, these birds alighted on oars or on the deck of the launch, showing absolutely no fear of a man in a boat.

Usually one bird incubated while its mate was away fishing. In one case the male booby, recognizable by the small size of the pupils of his eyes, was standing by the nest and flew off at once. The sitting bird allowed me to look at her eggs and then suddenly seemed to realize that she should be afraid; so forthwith, with no effort, she ejected a fourteen-inch flying fish and flew away. She had apparently just come in from fishing and had taken her place on the nest while her unfed mate was ready to start to sea. I salvaged the fish, for it was quite fresh and a perfect specimen. The booby returned within two minutes after I left her nest.

In another instance the ejected fish was partly digested. I went a little way off and watched the indignant bird waddle back, and although the unpleasant morsel was covered with sand until it looked like a breaded veal chop, she swallowed it with gusto, sand and all, and settled again upon her egg.

The distinction in voice between the sexes was as marked as that of pupil diameter. When the female booby was taking her turn on the eggs, she resented my approach with a squawk or quack like one of the hoarse notes of a barnyard hen, or perhaps more like the voice of a duck, but much deeper. The next bird to be encountered would differ in outward appearance only in the small pupil, but his warning cry, when uttered, would be merely a ridiculously high, shrill *peeeeeeep!* like the call of an overgrown chick.

The syrinx, or voice box, of the young boobies and the full-grown female has rounded dilations of bone at the juncture of the trachea, but this character disappears in the adult male bird. Here we have an exact relation between voice and the structure of the vocal organ, for the high, squeaky voice of the male parent is evidently on the way to obliteration.

The frigate birds regularly rob the boobies of their hard-earned food; I know in several cases the victimized birds had to catch twice again as many fish before they could escape to their nests with an adequate meal. Once when Crocker was fishing from the launch, he had an unusual experience with one of these robbers. A frigate bird swooped down, gently lifted the flying-fish bait and carried it twenty feet aloft. There the bird held it, slowly following the boat, regulating his speed exactly to that of the launch, until after several minutes of skillful manipulation he disengaged the fish from the hook. He then swallowed the morsel and flew off as nonchalantly as if he and his ancestors had always fed in this manner. When a feather jig was put on, a booby began to follow and watch it, while the same frigate bird, ready to rob him, trailed along many feet up in the air. But the booby soon detected the falseness of the lure and left it.

Near the end of the sandy beach and well inland we found large colonies of tree-nesting, red-footed boobies, perhaps five hundred birds in all. For their encampment they had chosen the only groups of good-sized bushes in the lowlands of Clarion, a small compact mass of euphorbias, all well guarded by cactus. Although there were three separate colonies, the solid, terrible phalanx of cactus permitted a near approach to only one. Dozens of last year's birds in brown plumage took to flight as we approached, leaving the white adults sitting upon their well-built nests, with young in all stages of growth. Some were just hatched, with a straggly gray covering of scanty down which left them quite unprotected. The next stage was of birds like powder puffs, little balls of white swan's-down with protruding lead-colored beaks and bright beady eyes. They were vitally interested in everything which went on around them, and especially in ourselves, visions which must have been wholly beyond their experience.

The nests were close together, almost touching, and each parent had an unending feud with every neighbor. There seemed to be a tendency to blame the worry about our presence upon one another, and the nearer we came to any particular section, or any one branch or bush, the more intense became the rioting in that vicinity.

Some of the older nestlings looked larger than their parents, the fluffy character of the down making the size appear a third greater than it actually was. The voices of this species reminded us of the maddening, whirling, raucous rattles so dear to the hearts of revelers on New Year's Eve.

I saw a burrowing owl take to wing and fly up a dark gully in the heart of the booby colony. A number of these little owls had their homes underground immediately beneath the nests of the sea birds. They were the most delightful of all the island birds and almost as tame as the boobies. Whether perched in the top of a dead branch or in the grass runway at the entrance of their burrow, they greeted the human invaders with a series of bobbing curtsies which seemed so much a welcome that one felt like bowing in return. Crocker and Toshio captured a female and its nearly full-grown young, and the latter is now bowing and scraping to visitors at the Zoological Park of the New York Zoological Society, the first Clarion burrowing owl ever to reach New York alive.

When we come to any place new and strange, whether city, desert, or island, our attention at first is attracted and held by the loudest noises, the most brilliant colors, the most bizarre forms. If the scene is an island such as Clarion, and our object the study of

the living creatures, the first few days pass in a turmoil of distracted activities and impressions. Then the fever of uncorrelated
observation and indiscriminate collecting dies down. There comes
to eye or ear some minor overtone, the first of a host of details, infinitely more lasting and significant than the more blatant sensory
signals. Out of the chaos of fleeting first impressions arise intrinsic
patterns of colors, odors, voices, movements, habits — the vital and
necessary mosaic which ultimately must mirror the scene and place
to writer and reader.

On the twelfth of May, after watching the *Zaca* start dredging
in the open sea, we set out confidently at low water for the real
tide pools of Clarion, and at once felt the teeth of the island's
inimical spirit, a spirit which seemed to challenge and block every
attempt at scientific investigation. Here were most excellent pools
full of fish, pools hidden behind a high barrier of craggy rocks. We
unlimbered and immediately were startled by a thunderous explosion from some place invisible, and a second later a perfect deluge of foam and water descended upon us and upon the pools,
which instantly overflowed their rims. So abrupt was the cliff outside and so powerful the surf that only a slight difference in density
and consistency of water particles distinguished high from low tide.
We had to give up serious tide-pool work except in a few rare lo-
cations.

Leaving the geysered pools, we climbed a high cliff and found a
precarious seat on the edge between the solid culture of low impenetrable cacti behind and a sheer drop to the waves beneath. A
few feet beyond where I sat was a bit of color as startling to the eye
as a loud cry would be to the ear — a rock covered with a solid unbroken sheet of orange-ocher lichen, with a turquoise lizard draped
over one rim as only the lizard or a Hokusai could do it, a dual force

and harmony of pigment which a priori would be thought impossible.

Leaving the pools behind, I climbed down to the shore, and shedding everything but trunks and sneakers, crept as close as I dared to the seething, crashing waters. The mollusks were few and far between, and to find them I had to go to the outermost rocks. Here in the very zone of the smashing water were giant chitons and limpets. The former could usually be reached if I chose carefully between incoming waves, slipped a knife edge between rock and shell, levered it up, and scrambled back to some secure hold while the foam washed over me. The limpets almost without exception were beyond human reach.

The thin amount of life under stones or between them was very noticeable. This too was due to the ceaseless pounding, and any movable rock was constantly shifted and rolled, gathering no animal moss or life of any kind. There were many potholes with one or two stones at the bottom, and the smoothness and depth of these attested the tremendous and eternal stirring force of the ocean's contact with this isolated isle.

Almost every one of the few organisms had had to dig itself in, to resist being torn away and destroyed. The rare long-spined urchins were withdrawn into deep crevices with their mass of needle spines compressed into a very narrow segment. The short-spined ones were deeply embedded in coral or in actual lime rock — prisoners forever, but safe from death by wave force. The only living creatures active and free on the naked rocks were the ever-present scarlet crabs which flattened and gripped with all their sharp claws, defying the heaviest surf.

We kept on along the coast and by accident discovered and passed through a veritable slit of an entrance to an enclosed, lovely, rocky area. Here was a pool which, at least for an hour at low tide, was free from direct attack on the part of the waves. Before and after this scant duration of time, the surges made the entrance impossible and the pool a caldron.

Frank, armed with tethered harpoon, had disappeared through a second cleft, humming some Samoan song whose minor quavers came to us above the low distant roar. We were left alone and for a time remained dry enough to give some attention to details of the life around us. The overhanging cliff shut off all the breeze, and this rocky room, floored with the pool and ceilinged with heaven, was quiet. In it Clarion forgot itself and slept. The pool became a window and all its secrets plain.

From its surface rose eight monsters, temporarily quiescent in lava, their black heads protruding in a sort of fearful school. The most ordinary was amazingly like the head and snout of a bull elephant seal, while the nomenclature of the rest would tax the imagination of a Syme-*cum*-Dunsany. One was unquestionably a mipt! Their absence of motion only added to the sinister effect, enhancing the idea of waiting for something. The riffle of a restless fish set their shadows moving, and everyone knows that the shadow of a monster is more awful than its substance.

The most colorful of the pool people were demoiselles, which were earthen brown on the fore part of the body, changing gradually to hyacinthine blue set off by brilliant yellow eyes. The most abundant — the minnows of Clarion — were the silvery *Kuhlias* (they have no common name) with their black-and-white-banded tail fins, flashing when they turned, like the flag of a rabbit. A school of friendly old abudefdufs mingled with as many pale-green surgeons, whose narrow vertical black lines contrasted with the broader ones of the sergeant majors. Little else was visible until I threw in a hook baited with a toothsome snail. Instantly there came a rush from under a rock, and a rainbow wrasse hooked himself. The hook went back and the same thing happened. All the others which swam about in full view bit with interest but with no vim — tentative nibbles which saved their lives but exhibited no individuality. But the green and violet and ocher and blue glories in scales kept hidden until the bit of snail came into sight.

Close behind me two Clarion doves cooed in some anxiety, for their rough nest of fine sticks and grass was in a crevice ten feet overhead. There were no eggs as yet, but spring had come to Clarion, as witness the turtles and whales. The doves looked much like our mourning doves with considerable white to the tips of the tail feathers and several black spots on the shoulders. In addition there was a touch of cerulean around their eyes, a green of "burnished iris" on the neck, while the legs and feet were of delicate coral. The note, too, was very like that of our New England pastures.

We went around the pool to pass farther to the west through another opening, when I saw a wren fly up from an overhanging cliff with a caterpillar in her beak. I walked as near as the cliff would permit and looked up, and there was an untidy mass of delicate grass stems wedged into a crevice well out of our reach. The wren soon left and perched on top of a mass of rough red lava, and sang. As I have said before, it was only partly wrenlike — a fine wire of a song, a short but drawn-out zizzing, then a catch, and a brief varied end. It vibrated loudly in this rocky room. The wren's home was within sight of the dove's nest, and from where I stood, I could just see a third Clarion home, indicated by the head of a white booby, brooding on the cliff from which we had come.

From this quiet home of the dove and the wren we crept through Frank's gorge and seemed in another world. Here were three jagged capes reaching out and splitting the onrushing surges, blocking their ceaseless efforts to wipe Clarion out of existence. Not a dry rock summit was to be seen, and all except the very ridge ran white with a hundred cascades after every wave. We crawled out, found saddlelike contours which we could grip with knees and thighs as we would a bucking horse, and here we tried hook-and-line fishing. Great whales spouted and gamboled in mad, titanic courtship just outside the reef, and beyond them the *Zaca* slowly dragged her slender wire thread back and forth.

Boobies swooped overhead and scarlet Sally lightfoots skittered over the rocks, and always the foam and spray crashed around us and washed up until we were in a slather waist-deep, trying to salvage our fishlines and keep our balance on the sharp, slippery surfaces. In every swirling green and white mass I could see the water-filtered purple of blue jacks, the orange of the angelfish, and the black of great groupers. In spite of lost tackle and the fight to keep our seats, we caught one of each species. The moment the hook sank to the bottom it tangled in the short prickly coral, but this was the only place we found where direct contact could be made between shore and offshore rocks.

Now and then I would get an abstract vision of my present cosmos, and see myself on this bit of volcano tip above the two miles plus of ocean depth, with the next nearest land more than two hundred miles away — a minute dot in mid-ocean and I a veriest pygmy, striving to wrest a few secrets from an environment so difficult and so alien to humankind: the rocks where the least slip gashed our flesh, or the surging water into which a fall would mean instant death. In the midst of this steely hardness and knifelike sharpness lived and gently sang the wren and the dove.

CHAPTER 11

Going Ashore

BANDERAS Bay is so large that in small maps of Mexico it is usually the only bay given a name throughout the entire western coast, south to Panama. Its very size and open character made it one of the least interesting of the forty-odd we were to visit. When the high mountains first came into view in early morning, I examined the chart spread out on the deckhouse, and suddenly an early geography lesson came vividly to mind. I had been asked what cape on the North American continent was the most mumble-mumble? And I had answered, "Cape Corrientes." It was the correct answer, but I was reprimanded and made to repeat the word because I gave it an inexcusable rolling of the r's, in imitation of what I had heard was the Spanish pronounciation. I now raised my head, looked at the great promontory, and shouted, "Cabo Corrrrrrrrientes!" exactly as I had a half century before. I waited, but this time there was no reprimand, although there ensued sarcastically solicitous questions as to my sanity.

After traversing the great bay, we slowly drew up to our anchorage, which was any place where our chart and constant lead heaving showed to be over twelve fathoms, and a mile or more from the shore. Customs were quick because they consisted only of a bow, a salutation, a drink, a cigar, and a signature. Here, as in many other places to come, there was no trouble, no suspicion, but an insatiable curiosity on the part of the customs officer to see a real yacht from topsail to toilet.

Leaving the captain to do the honors, we all went ashore. This latter is the correct word, for the small Mexican town of Peñas boasts no wharf. I should hazard a guess that all imports to Peñas from the sea must be waterproof, or of a higher specific gravity than saline H_2O. The surf was rather high, but when we leaped out at the psychological moment with cameras and nets held on high, we were only overshoe.

The country and surrounding mountains showed the usual semi-arid type which characterizes so much of western Mexico. We walked through street after street and up the tiny *rio* to the south side. There we crossed the stream on the most spindling and shaky of swing bridges. It dangled in mid-air yards above the marshy trickle, doubtless measured to extreme flood season when the omnipresent debris of dead tree trunks must have hurtled down from the highlands. The birds set the key to the country: grackles and silver-beak tanagers in the town, perching hawks watching fearlessly, filled with curiosity, while black and turkey vultures scrutinized us hopefully for signs of early demise. There were, besides, large blue kingfishers, kiskadees, small green macaws in threes, and finally a pair of glorious scarlets.

Quickly as we had come ashore, walked out into the country and returned, underground gossip channels had caught up with us, and a small urchin would shyly approach and offer an unfortunate lizard, usually tailless, or a still more ruined butterfly. Most of the houses were rather tumble-down, patched with gasoline tins and bits of rusty corrugated iron, but frequently through half-open doors we caught glimpses of splashes of brilliantly colored flowers in rear patios. Now and then a house was sandwiched in which actually had a painted façade and bright gingham curtains in the windows. From these leaned forth attractive painted wenches who passed the time of day with us as we sauntered by. Even here the strange tale of our interests had penetrated, and one scarlet-cheeked girl, with the mongoloid cheekbones and slant eyes of an Indian, vanished, and when she reappeared, held out to me a shell. I recognized it as one for which we had searched in Guadalupe and found only one. I drew forth money to pay for it, but she waved it aside with a smile and said, "*Nada dinero; es solamente un juguete para un niño.*" She persistently refused, so the "*niño*" accepted his "toy" with gratitude, and made his best Spanish manners. It would be embarrassing to have to give to this desirable orange-hearted turban shell a specific locality label.

We passed old, old Indians gossiping on the corners, men making fish nets, one really lovely elderly woman sitting at the entrance of her house with unself-conscious tears streaming down her cheeks as she seemed to be mumbling prayers. Now and then unbelievably tiny naked infants, on seeing us, walked, crept, or ran with all the force of their chubby legs to escape from our path. Some were patently terrified, but none wept.

We went to the old, half-finished, half-ruined cathedral which was begun many years ago, and in 1929 the people had somehow scraped together fifty thousand pesos to complete it. Then the revolution came and the soldiers took it all. Now the blind windows are stopped with sacking and the great, curved, rose-to-be window at the back of the altar is blocked by a thin film of thatch. Tanagers and sparrows are nesting in the altar framework, yet the bell rings the hours and calls to Mass. A sign warns all females to cover their heads and dress with modesty before entering.

A few yards beyond the church we were astonished to see an ancient automobile, of ripe vintage but newly painted. There were four men on their backs underneath it, attempting either to assemble or to fasten it together. The story was that it had been carried thither on the backs of numberless peons and deposited here, although in Peñas the passable stretches of navigable roads could be measured by yards. Standing around were cowboys garbed as for some Hollywood rodeo, with elaborate saddles on the tiniest of horses, enormous revolvers and often two exceedingly heavy belts of cartridges, bright sashes and top-heavy sombreros of more than Oriental splendor, together with spurs of a size fairly to puncture the diminutive *caballos*. On their faces were amused grins, and I am sure that among their soft phrases must have been the Mexican equivalent of "Get a horse!"

A small boy volunteered information which completed the evolution of transportation. He said that beyond the little stream, out of sight, was a landing field to which an airplane came now and then from Guadalajara. Here were peon, horse, car, and plane, and the most useful of all was the peon.

We returned along the sea front where there was a promenade of sorts, consisting of a rough walk, with benches rapidly reverting to their original elements. Here, at the sign of Manzanillo Cerveza, six musicians played the wildest, most fascinating of *rumbas*, and girls in spangles danced on the tables, being more smooth than the surrounding stone floor. From the shore, unending lines of burros clambered up, laden with panniers of great rounded beach stones which, with inadequate mortar, were meant for the walls of new houses. I was sitting on the doorstep of the single-roomed customs house when I felt a soft, moist nose nuzzling under my arm. Twisting around, I found a half-grown peccary begging for a piece of the *dulce* which I was eating. I scratched its side and the little creature immediately rolled over on its back, grunting with ecstatic joy.

We had "done" Peñas. There was nothing wildly exciting or unexpected about it all, and it was one of the most impoverished little places I ever visited. Yet our memory of it was almost perfect, of a charm of utterly unspoiled simplicity. Again and again it seemed as if the tableau in every street had been carefully arranged for a Hollywood set. As for being stared at, or annoyed by undue attention, we might have been invisible. And yet to many of the inhabitants we must have seemed as strange and amusing as actors in circus or cinema.

As we started for our boat, the sun sank exactly at the southern tip of the bay, and I shouted aloud, "*Adios, Cabo Corrrrrrientes!*" much to the amusement of a dozen Peñasians within hearing. Only the customs house official, now in mufti shirt and trousers, shorn of all the regalia of officialdom, rushed after me to salvage his pet peccary, which had evidently lost his heart to me and my *dulce*, and was preparing to follow me through sand and water into the boat.

Our first real Mexican town was sound asleep at half past two on the hot afternoon of *Domingo*, November 21. It was Manzanillo, and it was one big siesta. We, like "mad dogs and Englishmen," disregarded the blazing heat and clambered up and down the hills, to no evident result scientifically, but to the betterment of our evaporation pores. To these steep slopes clung rather pitiful dwelling places, fashioned by peons too poor to include a patio. But in place of this enclosed heart of beauty, there was always a box or gasoline tin with some flowering plant culled from somewhere, often only a wizened geranium, dusty and droopy, but with a brave blossom. A scattered sound of pigs was all that greeted us, rushing out from beneath the huts of wattled clay. Yet each house had a rough cage from which a sleepy parrakeet or tanager watched us through one somnolent eye. Indolent snakebirds perched in the mangroves, and great yellow flycatchers rested on bare branches, too hot and lazy even to *kiskadee!* for us. Another tropical note was a few heliconian butterflies whose slow, languid flight emphasized the general Sunday torpidity. After almost falling through a disreputable bridge, we returned to the *Zaca*.

After dinner we again went ashore, and the double magical wand of coolness and night had worked wonders. The place seethed with life, noise, and activity. We went to the main plaza and drank doubtful *cerveza* from dubious glasses. At an adjoining table three desperados, armed at every possible point, sucked ice-cream sodas through wilted, secondhand straws, and obviously made the drinks last as long as possible.

Their attention was wholly concerned with two of the three double lines of promenaders, passing and repassing. The center stream, consisting of men only, resembled a dark line in the spectrum, bounded by two intensely brilliant ones, for the two remaining files of Mexican *señoritas* were ablaze with gorgeous colors and patterns.

Five bands were playing at once and all well within the sound of each other's instruments. One, in a bus, advertising a cinema, "The Robin Hood of Mexico," provided the elements of crescendo and diminuendo in this quintet of orchestras, as the bus approached the plaza or receded. The ensemble, although occasionally overpowering, was rather pleasant. Two bands, vying with one another, would have been most objectionable, one's sense of rhythm being monopolized first by one, then the other. But when five are operating simultaneously, one has no choice but to attend to the pandemonium as a whole, and actually it was not unpleasant, and not overwhelmingly noisy. Many of the more strident chords seemed to soften or obliterate each other.

In front of a large cafeteria, in a cleared space, was the second orchestra, a sort of hybrid Spanish-*cum*-jazz affair. Here, for the small sum of fifty centavos, one could dance apparently all night, with intervals of relaxing and drinking. Strange tangos were the specialty of this group, and for five minutes we watched a small urchin perform amazingly, with hands held tightly behind his back, a cross between a *rumba* and a dervish whirl. In the center of the plaza was the official band, which provided classical entertainment, under the baton of a maestro with the incredible name of Jesús C. Pilato. His directing had such temperament that the sound effects either dominated all the four other assemblages, or else became utterly inaudible. From where we sat this resulted in the quaint appearance of a director and his musicians in full play, making motions wholly out of tempo with some strident hot jazz tune, which for the moment held the upper hand.

From a large tent at one side of the plaza still another band alternately blared forth and became silent while a villainous-looking barker roared through a tin loud-speaker that at nine-thirty of the clock the grand drama *La Dama de las Camelias* would be presented, with the assurance that with the part of Margarita played by the *aplaudida* Luisa Velasco, it was indubitably *"éxito seguro!"* and as to its respectability, it was *"espectáculo propio para familias."*

Thus assured, we decided to attend, and for a peso each were led to the luneta, a line of string-seated chairs. Along the sides of the tent were the *grados* (apparently Mexican for bleachers) well filled with, judging by facial expressions and costumes, Indians, cutthroats, Aztecs, pirates, babies at the breast or not, conquistadores and ladies of Spain. Every face was a study, some scarred and stamped with the fear of life, others with the profiles straight from a Mayan stele, now and then a very lovely face, but all vitally absorbed in everything. The center aisle was, for some reason, beloved of stray dogs, which crept under the tent, and performed absorbing acrobatic feats of flea-scratching.

A trio, violin, piano and drums, played the overture to *Poet and Peasant* and did it very well. Then the curtain went up knee-high to the actor on the stage, and simultaneously the government band, just outside, broke forth in something of Wagnerian force. The curtain descended abruptly and noisily, and soon the plaza band stopped and chose some softer theme which allowed the voices of the actors to be heard.

We stayed through two scenes, performed most heartily by the leading actress. Amid a nation and an audience of brunettes, the observation that Luisa Velasco was blonde is an understatement. She reminded me somewhat of Lillian Russell, but a Lillian Russell with an added number of pounds avoirdupois which I hesitate to estimate. She was clothed in a dress of cloth of silver, and one was impelled to the belief that the only possible method of introduction into it was by a process of pouring. The gasp of genuine awe from the *grados* when the silver Margarita, after rather audibly mounting the back-curtain stairs, appeared on the stage, must have meant that the word Madonna took on, for many, a new and a very definite connotation.

The stage was ridiculously small, and when Margarita crossed L to R, the floor bent alarmingly. Yet she must have been an unusually talented actress in her prime, and nothing in the embarrassingly limited surroundings affected her performance. She was very good, and as wholly undisturbed by her audience of desperados, Indians, babies, and dogs, as well as itinerant gringos, as if she were giving a command performance. One of the minor actors spilled a glass of wine on the seat of the only chair, and in the course of two long speeches Luisa deftly dropped her handkerchief, a newspaper, and the cover from a small table onto the chair before she trusted her frock to its damp seat. The clothes of the leading man were many sizes too big for him, yet he skillfully shook his hands free of the enveloping sleeves when the gestures demanded their appearance. Wherever Dumas had written in a kiss, the resouding smack was greeted by the occupants of the *grados* with a hearty murmur of approval, while some voice would petition, "*Un otro!*" But the attention of the entire audience never wavered, and we led the applause with enthusiasm and fervor. One very noticeable thing was the perfect Castilian Spanish diction of the leading members of the cast. There would have been no *z*'s in Luisa's *cerveza*, if she would condescend to speak of so lowly a beverage.

As I made my way back to the yacht, I thought of Luisa Velasco with great pity. The sunset of such an actress is not pleasant, and yet the sincerity of the whole — bands, performance, audience — made it all admirable. And under trying conditions she held her audience, even though only a fraction could have known what it was all about; Bernhardt could not have done more.

When we reached the *Zaca* this same evening, the sight at the submarine night light kept us concentrated for a long time. About the glow of the bulb was the usual dense mass of small fry, all going clockwise, full speed. Close outside their orbit was another zone of life, outdoing even the rings of Saturn, for this circle was moving anticlockwise. For a time I had no idea what the fish were, for to our dim eyesight, looking down from the deck, there appeared to be thousands of the thinnest lines of silver, all shooting ahead in a wheel of life, at a mad, furious pace. A dozen of these outsiders suddenly turned obliquely inward, each seized a small fish and banked outward again. As they moved from their place, they turned sideways, and the lines became full silvery plaques — moonfish — the thinnest, roundest, silveriest things imaginable. Usually one is seen, or at most a few together, but here all the ocean seemed to have given up its hordes of lunar constellations, and the multitude had become magnetized by our little glow.

I pulled the lamp slowly above the water, and the moonfish closed in, overrunning the smaller inner fry, looking like diminutive replicas of all moon reflections in the water since time began. Finally, they broke the surface, forgetting their hunger and everything, impelled to follow upward by the luminous spell of the strange gleam. When the light descended again, they quieted down and resumed their eternal whirling. We took a flashlight photograph, and this sudden momentary increase of illumination frightened them all into the surrounding darkness, but in two minutes all were back. When I held the light clear of the surface for three minutes the multitude of fry had gone for good, but the moonfish then closed in, and when I went down to my cabin, the thousands upon thousands filled every visible area of water. A final glance ashore showed the last lights of Manzanillo flickering out, and I thought of Luisa Velasco in her cloth of silver, and I thought of the mad, but equally brilliant moonfish, and I rejoiced in the grand thing which we call diversity of interest in this life of ours and on earth.

A quick run ashore the following morning showed Manzanillo rather threadbare without its tinsel veneer of night and electric light, and we saw many of our new friends somewhat the worse for wear. There was no bank, so I changed some money at the house of a Portuguese who unlocked the padlock of his rusty safe with a nail. The test of a Latin-American town is its market, and this one was small and poor. This was one of our bays, to be sure, lagoon and all, but in the blatant glare of day we found that man had left it little of visible charm.

Bermuda is undoubtedly the apex of a mighty volcanic mountain

The bird blind at South Beach, Nonsuch, and the giant binoculars
in action

Nestling cahow from Green Island

Parent cahow

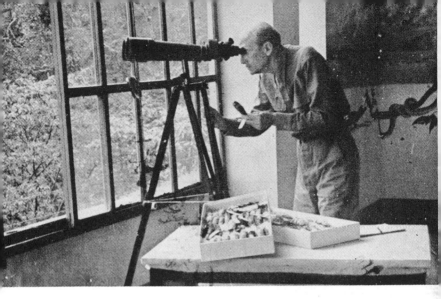

Giant binoculars; watching and naming birds a half mile away

The greatest danger we have ever experienced in contour dives was this tall reef which towered up suddenly, and up and over which we were drawn just in time to escape its jagged cliffs. Just beyond is seen the old Bermudian glacial beach. Painted by Helen Tee-Van

Our forty-two-foot whale shark swims quietly along the surface after being harpooned

Marooned with a seven-foot boa constrictor on the shore of Port Parker, Costa Rica

tling hoatzin climbing
th thumb and forefinger

Head of adult hoatzin

Hummingbird drinking from heliconia blossom

Binoculars and plaster cast at Portachuelo Pass

Tree fern in the cloud forest of Portachuelo Pass; shaking insects into an umbrella

Laura Schlageter painting air plants on the jungle floor

Jungle-pit method of collecting nocturnal jungle creatures

We had difficulty in getting permission to dredge in the harbor as we left, because the year before a Japanese battleship had asked to be allowed to drag for the body of a sailor who had fallen overboard, and then proceeded to take a complete series of soundings. The patient display and explanation of the published Manzanillo chart whereon were recorded every possible sounding which could be made, together with judicious use of liquid palliatives, soon cleared us of suspicion and made us free of the entire Mexican coast.

The first dredge came up quite barren except for sundry bottles and tins and a small, much annoyed puffer. But the second, of twenty minutes in one hundred and eighty feet, proved incredibly rich. Among a crowd of other organisms there were sixty of the pearl-bearing singing fish, and at least twenty species of rare crabs. We could not finish the sorting and describing, even with the deck lights, late at night, so stopped dredging and put to sea from sheer physical inability to tackle another haul.

CHAPTER 12
River of Mud

ACAPULCO slipped astern; our friends became one with the crowds on the wharf, houses shrank together, streets merged, the surrounding eternal hills lost substance and joined sea and sky in a blurred cloud on the horizon. We carried away few scientific specimens from this Mexican city, but a host of strange memories, written and unwritten, which will outlast many more concrete things. As the *Zaca* headed southward, we went up in the bow and looked ahead for whatever the sea had next to offer.

A great school of dolphins appeared from nowhere and acted as escort destroyers to our battleship, but with their speed and grace they made the *Zaca* a veritable crawling tub. We recalled a promise made to a distant curator of marine mammals, hardened our hearts, and bade Pemasa Utu get one. Looking at the great spindle-shaped creature on deck, streamlined and finned, it was as difficult as always for me to visualize a four-footed, furred, terrestrial ancestor of this mammalian fish. Its scientific destiny was fulfilled to the utmost in the preservation of its black and pied skin, skeleton, parasites, and food.

Old Earth rolled around and sank the sun in a glory of gold and red, and early the next morning, coming on deck, I found old

Earth still rolling, and bringing up from the sea the selfsame sun in a reverse but equally breath-taking glory of red and gold. It was the rainless season, but from a black-rimmed cloud, low hung over the distant land, rain was pouring in oblique streaks, like the parallel hairlines on a diffraction grating. My first surprise at this unreasonable sight was changed to a sudden realization that the distant coast of southern Mexico was still rainless. This rainstorm was solely a heavenly affair, the drops, like the sparks from a spent rocket, dying in mid-air, cloud to cloud, watering we knew not what celestial mirage of some invisible skyscape. To the parched land beneath, it was only the momentary shadow of a passing cloud, a swift meteorological sleight of hand, a Tantaluslike precipitation and absorption, now you see it, now you don't. And far below, dusty petals crackled, birds panted with parched thirst, and the cacti, watery misers, hugged their humid stores close within their pads.

It was still early on this last day of November when our anchor chain rattled down through eight fathoms. On Toshio's ever-ready lines four catfish came almost as quickly to the surface, up from the bottom, and swung overside, squeaking and protesting after their bewhiskered fashion. Our chart told us that we were at the mouth of an indentation, almost too shallow to be called a bay, into the head of which emptied the Rio Dulce. *Dulce* it might well be, but to the eye it was also *Rio Muy Sucio*, as heralded by the squeaking catfish. It seemed to promise poor hunting for our mental fish larder, but ere this we had plucked plums — or is it figs — from apparent thistles, and the most bromidic mind knows that lilies spring from no more promising mud than that which stained the sea about us with deltoid fans of opacity. So we took the otter boat and the pram and started hopefully for the River of Sweetness.

From a collection of miserable thatched huts huddled behind a mud bar at the mouth of the stream, there came forth a *jefe* of sorts in a dugout. The crew seemed to be working in shifts, some pulling ragged strokes with oars of assorted lengths, and an equal number bailing with more energy than is usually manifested by Mexican peons. Documents were demanded of us, but without much conviction or desire. We compromised amicably with several dozen cigarettes, their tissue-paper envelopes apparently more acceptable than any letters of marque we might proffer. We also saved the rowers from imminent drowning by towing them back to the village.

As we chugged upriver, fish came occasionally to the surface with a glance in our direction which might have been interpreted as begging us to remove them from their suffocating environment. We would have been glad to comply, but the absolute turbidity, combined with the exceedingly swift current, enforced a total ignorance of the ichthyological content which, I fear, will still be unbroken on the day of our death.

We looked about us with envy. We were merely Lords of Creation going against the current in a complex launch, while all about us were Better Fishers than we were, Gunga Din. We watched snakebirds submerge quietly and come up with a fish speared through by both mandibles; we saw gannets plummet, guided by some sort of magical mud vision, and emerge with mulletlike prey held pincerwise. And finally, like the helpless humans which we were, we coveted the automatic casting of the pelican's trap. He lifted his head, his beak positively drooling small fry, and we could not even perch on his back, like the small gulls, and snatch the scaly crumbs which fell from the great bird's beak.

However, being at heart that thing barely tolerated by Ultimate Scientists — a Naturalist — my allegiance, impelled by environmental sour grapes, turned from Saint Walton to Saint Audubon, and in the twinkling of an eye my mind's interest, accelerating past evolutions, shifted from fish to birds. With unichthyological facility, I unlimbered my glasses and reveled in the flocks which rose from water, bank, and trees as we went on up the stream, now become *el Rio de Pájaros*.

Having been an ornithologist most of my life, the mental observing and recording of every flying thing had long since passed the conscious stage and joined the pleasant group of involuntary actions, together with winking and breathing. In order that a book such as this may inspire a voluntary desire of ownership on the part of something more than a dozen readers, I suppress my instinctive wish to include every such list of birds. But the avian fauna of the Rio Dulce was really exceptional, and representative of many other favored places along this west coast, so I yielded to my craving. As the sodden dope fiend reaches with trembling hand for just one more sniff of "snow," so I use this excuse for one grand list of birds, and right in the text, too.

An intensification of tropicalness was apparent in this place, and there was just enough of open water, swamps, and shrubs, with alternating clumps of high, dry cactus areas and lower almost-forest, to attract and sustain a large number of birds.

For the first time on this trip we saw brilliant color in large masses, rafts of floating water hyacinths dappled with purple and gold standards, and trees of solid yellow bloom. A good omen was a freshly emerged *Junonia coenia*, or some unimportant subspecies, waving its wings from a hyacinth leaf. In varying sizes and degrees of paleness and intensity of color and pattern this delightful little butterfly has waited for my coming in all parts of the world. In my boyhood New England I made its acquaintance, and it was Number 3 in my very first collection. I knew it and know it as *Junonia coenia.* With utter and happy disregard for specificity or newly unearthed generic names, regardless of subspecies, forms, varieties, and aberrations, I always whisper or scream or think *Junonia coenia* when and wherever it again comes into view. In Bermuda it is small and keeps to the ground and low shrubs out of the force of the wind; in the Himalayas it is also small, but, like the flowers of those lofty heights, unusually brilliant in color.

Returning to our Rio Dulce, besides the deltic village, there was a scattering of huts and dilapidated *casas* along the banks. But, as elsewhere, this was a land of poverty-stricken peons. *Caballeros* carry a well-sharpened machete and a revolver or two, and are draped with pounds upon pounds of cartridges, in belts, both horizontal and oblique, all ready, if need be, to decimate their fellows. But none here could afford shotguns or shells, and fish hatcheries were unheard of, so no excuse offered for the slaughter of fish-eating birds as in more civilized countries.

In my flaunted bird list I give only common names, for except in a few instances the species are self-evident at first glance of the bird-in-the-bush.

To remove the curse from an unadorned bird list, I want to look at the feathered natives of Rio Dulce first as essentially water birds, and second as doing their fishing in interestingly individual ways. If half a hundred men should start fishing with hand lines and worms in this river, they would doubtless catch a good lot of a few kinds, but when these became rare or wary, the fishermen would starve. Along comes a man with a casting net, or a dry fly, or a spoon, or a baited wire trap, and each becomes at once eminently successful. If all the hand-liners starved to death except a handful, then they and all the others would continue to make a good living. Next a sneak thief would creep along the bank and snitch fish from the creels, and he would prosper in his way. This apparently silly parable becomes stark reality when we apply it to the fishing birds of this little river.

The fishers we saw at the entrance, both before and after crossing the bar, seemed to put a maximum of energy and pep into their methods. In a scant three feet of water, two bombs dropped close alongside the boat. They were duds as far as bombs were concerned, but in both cases a big brown booby emerged with a shining fish in its beak. It labored up and off, and while still dripping salt water, gave itself a sudden twist, oriented the fish, and let it slide into its final resting place. That was the end of that, we thought; but no, one of the birds hurtled back upon its trail, and shot past us again, horizontally this time, with a great, bent-winged man-o'-war bird in terrific but effortless pursuit. Twice the booby dodged and doubled, but it was like trying to escape one's shadow. Finally it tried altitude, but this was fatal, and the frigate bird seemed to shake gravitation from its wings and fairly fall upwards. Just as it soared, ready to drop on its victim, the harassed booby surrendered. The fish, which we thought had passed forever from sight, appeared again, apparently as good as ever, and did a nose dive which no flying fish could imitate. A zigzag streak of sable lightning followed, picked the fish delicately from mid-air only a few feet above the surface, daintily swallowed it, and scooped up a chaser of salt water. In the distance the lightened booby disappeared in high gear, mad and hungry if ever any bird was. A feathered harpoon and a high-air robber had performed the prelude to our anglers' sonata. Rio Dulce's bar blazed with emotion: we were vitally interested and excited, the booby was disconsolate, the frigate bird was triumphant, and the fish — well, he probably thought no more about it. As Bret Harte has said, "The subsequent proceedings interested him no more." In human ethics the booby was an honest toiler, the frigate bird a reprehensible robber. But who are we to pass judgment outside our own field of action? Like the fish, who are we to worry?

It was not until we were coming out of the river later in the day that we saw a replica of the robber incident, but one which, to the spectator, was leavened with humor and devoid of rancor. A flock of brown pelicans were using their pouches and themselves as living cast nets, and making fine hauls of silver fry just inside the bar. With them were a quartet of laughing gulls, packing themselves full of dribbling fish. Again and again they would perch on the backs or tops of the heads of the pelicans and seize every stray fishlet as it trickled out of the corners of the draining beak. We could actually see the great birds looking down their noses at their diminutive, impudent, gate-crashing penny snatchers, but they were helpless to resent anything until they had swallowed their enormous mouthful. There seemed, indeed, no especial ill will on the part of the pelicans.

Even my Puritan ancestors would have been hard put to it to include the gulls and the frigate birds in the same hand-, or wing-, cuffed category of evil doers, and being safely separated from my first American ancestor by more than two hundred and ninety years and ten generations, I blatantly classed the acts of both birds as "bright and beautiful sin." In fact, I rather faintly damned the two fishers of the first part with the comforting dictum of Oscar Wilde, "There is no sin but stupidity."

Several flocks of terns, the smallest of all their kind, flew neatly in and out of the river, now and then imitating the method of the boobies, but more exquisitely and deftly, as a rapier to a broadsword.

Upriver we came to the first of the true anglers. Knee-deep across the river, or what in a heron is heel-deep, in the muddy water, was a pair of great blues. Always remember, I am speaking of species, not subspecies. By the slaughter of one of these splendid birds I could have called it with taxonomic precision *lessonii, wardi, treganzai, fannini,* or *sancti-lucae.* At fifty yards they were great, they were bluish and in general inseparable from my boyhood friends, so I was content. On this particular river trip *Ardea herodias* was good enough for me, and I am sure the patient herons shared my humor. Throughout all the time of passing I could not detect even the rolling of an eyeball, but before we disappeared, one bird took four steps and stabbed. I could see no result but a muddy splash.

The heron family now appeared en masse, but we must think of them first as fishers. Our Samoans could slip overboard and bring up from the bottom a live fish or a great basking turtle in their bare hands. In this they were like the booby or tern in using their entire body. The herons introduce the angler's methods; like a human fisherman in rubber boots, manipulating a rod and reel with hands alone, these birds use only their beak and neck. In the course of the river we saw nine species of herons, making ten altogether. There were snowy and American egrets, little blue herons, little green and Louisianas, bitterns, black- and yellow-crowned night herons and boatbills. The world's record for patient immobility must be given to the big egrets and the bitterns. They can outstylite Simeon Stylites and on a much smaller stance. In clear water they can at least see the approach of a prospective fish, but in the Rio Dulce the chances were infinitely against a fish breaking mud exactly at the spot where they were focused. Spearing fish through a small hole in the ice is my only adequate simile. I always have the feeling that a heron is posing for my special benefit and that after I leave, he does plenty of hustling about.

The smaller herons — snowy egrets, little blues and greens and Louisianas — are compressed to emaciation, and head on, to a fish, must look like amorphous colored cardboard. A correlation of this invisibility is less need for immobility, and we find the smaller birds stepping slowly and highly in a search for food. The little greens, whether along our millponds or in this tropical setting, have a procedure all their own. They have discarded patience for pursuit, and creep along the low branches of the mangroves or the shallows, and have even adopted the teetering or tail-tipping of rails, sandpipers, and water thrushes — a habit so unique that if classification were based on physical activities, little green herons would be removed quite out of their family and put into that of the rails. I have spoken of colored cardboard, and the edibility of this substance might be that of herons themselves for all the worry they give to predators. Some are white; others green, blue, or rufous; little blues are white in their youth, parti-colored in adolescence, and solid blue when grown up. I must say that if I were a hawk, the sight of the strong, sharp beak, the clutching feet and toes, and the thought of the scant coating of dry flesh on the bones of a heron would all help to ensure their immunity to attack.

Just as we humans go jack-lighting for fish at night, we saw from time to time, on this river, the big-eyed night herons waiting among the foliage for the dusk. With them was that absurd tropical cousin, the boatbill, with the beak of the other birds enlarged, rounded, made into a tiny model of the pelican idea.

Other birds began where the herons left off and brought to bear such ingenious instruments of prehension that it is a wonder the fish and worms do not vanish from the world. The ibises — white, scarlet, and glossy — probed the mud with their sensitive curved forceps, and the lovely roseate spoonbills sifted out unfortunate fish and other mud dwellers with sidewise swathes of their flat mandibles. The wood ibis — or, better, stork — was the dumbest-looking and the cleverest of all. He stood in the shallows, reached out one great foot, and with his toes carefully stirred up the mud and water, with beak poised ready to seize whatever attempted to escape. Cormorants often swim a few strokes underwater after their prey, but if I were a fish, I would dread the snakebird more than any other enemy. They seemed as much fish as fowl, they submerged so easily, and in addition to this facility they were fast swimmers and kept their beak closed. This latter habit meant that a single, quick, piercing stab was all that was needed.

Other fish eaters there were, but by accident, not by nature. These were the vultures — redheaded and black — which welcomed any stranded, ancient, dead fish, while even the small hawks, kiskadees, and grackles dipped down and picked up floating fry. Four ospreys passed over, but none dived. To these we give the anglers' banzai. No robbers or parasites they, but hunters with sufficient skill to dive, to snatch, and to rise, from air to water, to air again, lacking webs, clad in land birds' plumage, and making their capture with talons and toes alone.

I have not included the curlews, willets, stilts, and sandpipers, for they are rather worm chasers, and to catch a worm they, as we, simply go after it and dig. Doves, parrots, cuckoos, flycatchers, orioles, martins, and warblers — these filled the trees and the air with color or with song, but all their thoughts were on food far other than the dull-scaled inhabitants of the muddy current.

Next morning, heading ever southward, we realized how well protected this whole coast is against the intrusion of small vessels, and especially sailing ships. One of the most dangerous obstacles is man-made. A large steamer, the *San Francisco*, was wrecked here not many years ago, just south of the Rio Dulce, and the currents and general configuration of the coast resulted in a rapid and extensive silting up to within six or eight feet of the surface, so that today we find the great Tartar Shoals, seething with breakers, reaching out farther and farther for more prey to add to the submerged-steamer nucleus which like a pearl in an oyster, lies hidden in their heart.

Also, from here southward, for some hundreds of miles, vessels may suddenly, without warning, experience the terrible Tehuante-peckers. These are storms, northers, apparently connected in some way with the flattish, narrow Atlantic-Pacific isthmus at this point. A calm sea and a breathless air may turn, in less than half an hour, into a gale with cross seas fatal for any small boat. A Tehuante-pecker feels otherwise toward very tiny soft-winged moths, for after such a smashing storm, three of these, gray and mottled like fluttering bits of tweed, came straight out of the smother to our deck lamp, and there promptly expired from the heat. To avoid these unheralded hurricanes, it is necessary for ships such as the *Zaca* to hug the shore closely, thereby inviting destruction from the shoals. The alternative is to set the course fifty or more miles out to sea.

CHAPTER 13

A Touch of Purgatory

ON Thursday, the second day of December, the weather looking propitious (as Columbus might have said), we sped southward full speed. But the Evil Genius of Meteorology looked down, grinned at our hopefulness, and beckoned. Off came the Tehuante-pecker, and all day we rolled and pitched miserably. Work was impossible. We could only hold fast to anything within reach, lie impotently gazing at the active ceiling, or crawl futilely about, picking up a book and putting it down again. Under such circum-stances it is always profitable to marvel at the unbelievable activity of the Inorganic World — air, wind, water.

In late afternoon we were hurtled into a little bay, the Tehuan-tepecker dying away a few minutes after we were out of its reach. Doubtless in our present mental state, the Coast of Dis would have seemed a fair haven, but in the failing light the scene around us really seemed a very lovely place.

In this joyful aftermath of relaxation I got me an atlas and a chart, and the three of us went into a private conference. I found that twenty-two hundred and fifty miles west of the West Indian island of Dominica, on the Pacific coast of Mexico, is a series of three semiconnected bays which go by the grand names of Guatulco, Santa Cruz, and Tangola-Tangola. They are so small that on any moderate-sized map of Mexico they are not accorded the honor of the slightest tremor on the coast line. Even on the highest-powered chart, their names extend clear across their respective bays. So, on this December afternoon, we sailed into the northernmost of the trio, Guatulco. It was so diminutive that when halfway to the head, the *Zaca* had to be kedge-anchored fore and aft, to keep her from swinging too near the shore. Hardly had we passed the outermost headland with our Tehuantepecker howling derisively astern, when a ten-foot devilfish flew past us and rubbed against our bow as it went.

Early next morning we went to the head of the bay and landed through three slow, friendly breakers, which washed us high up on the beach and jettisoned us gently on the sand. As I stepped out, I saw at my feet a great bivalve absurdly like our boat, which also had been deposited without harm on this sandy slope. Three Mexicans appeared from a cluster of ramshackle huts and began to tie up great bundles of recently dried garfish. The fish were quite complete, with heads, tails, and odds and ends of entrails, and in addition to recently dried, I should have added half dried. They smelled to high heaven, yet the fishermen said they were headed inland to sell them. I wanted to ask many questions about this place, but the trio seemed in an urgent hurry, and shouldering, or, rather, heading, their odoriferous luggage, they set out, with an audible trail of humming flies following eagerly in their wake.

We walked about for a while, and suddenly became aware of the reason for the haste of the Mexicans. The beach as we saw it in early morning was as lovely as any idealized tropical shore: there were graceful flowering trees on low, overhanging cliffs, dropping their petals actually into the water of the sea; the sand was soft and of the whitest; the sky was a perfect blue; the air moved slowly in a gentle, soothing breeze. As I looked around, the whole world seemed a place of peace and delight. Well separated, we were walking slowly along the curve of sand when I suddenly saw my distant companions acting strangely. Two leaned over and slapped themselves in a sort of rhythmic dance; another ran swiftly up into the scrub; while a fourth dashed into the low breakers, shorts and all. Insanity seemed suddenly to have attacked the *Zaca's* staff. Then my bare legs began to tingle and sudden sharp pricks were felt. I looked down and saw the air, for two feet above the sand, foggy with uncountable midges, or sandflies. Call them what you will, we christened them with a whole new series of good Anglo-Saxon titles, doubtless merely adding to an already ample synonymy of extant Spanish *epítetos*.

I chose the scrub for sanctuary, and a dozen yards inland I left behind every member of the swarm. Their zone of influence was as circumscribed as their bodies were minute. As I skirted the beach beyond the reach of the organic flames, I saw, of course, things of beauty and interest — new shells, stranded, bleached skeletons of rare fish lying on the sand. At one place I ventured down. It did not seem possible that the apparently clear air, the uninhabited sand could harbor such agony. As I fled, it was like running the gantlet in old days of Indian torture, and the delighted whoops of my heartless friends enhanced the simile.

I caught hundreds of the insects in a single swoop of the net, and although most of them passed easily through the mesh, I bottled several and examined them on board.

Their eyes were iridescent emerald, thorax of oxidized bronze, abdomen of glowing amber, legs golden, shading into dark on thighs and feet, eight-jointed antennae coppery gold, and wings large and perfectly hyaline. In length they stretched 1.5 mm., or sixteen to the inch. They possessed a short innocent-looking beak, but it was a weapon which drove us frantic from the beaches, morning and evening, and our wounds required constant attention to avoid serious infection, to say nothing of sleepless nights. No wonder the Mexicans have established their town of Guatulco miles inland, away from the bay.

Mosquitoes seemed quite absent, but during the day the swarms of *Simuliidae*, or sand flies, made two beach trips all that we could tolerate. After our first day at Guatulco we were finely pitted with blood specks, and the swelling and itching became almost unbearable. The red bugs were bad in the shrub, but as usual I became gradually immune to them. Ticks also were present and added their enthusiastic attentions to our poor bodies, although taken alone, they would not have been a factor in the general unpleasantness. If we found a ready-made trail, all discomforts were nonexistent, but the moment we were tempted to turn aside, to push through the undergrowth, trouble started. The botanical barriers were much worse than in any northern desert. The candelabra cacti grew straight up and were walked around easily, but the ground for miles inland was covered with masses of half-dead fallen clusters of spines from the palmate types which here seemed to be almost creeping, and often hid the ground from view. Acacias with their varied assortment of spines blocked the edges of the cattle and burro trails, with such variations toward exquisite torture as the bull's-horn species, whose spines held you tightly, the while from their hollows, legions of stinging ants poured forth their formic acid and completed the purgatorial round. The second day at Guatulco I set this combination of vegetable and animal blitzkrieg into action when I attempted to go about twenty feet in an untrailed direction. I saw some birds on a flowering tree, but I never reached the tree.

The coast of this part of southern Mexico is really set apart, a halfway place of no definite classification, not wholly desert and far from qualifying as fertile tropical, yet with features of each in their most unpleasant aspects. It had a real interest because of the actual uncertainty of its facies, but it was heavily defended from patient, prolonged scrutiny by most adequate barriers, as far as man was concerned.

When we were driven from the scrub by static obstacles, and from the beach by exceedingly active ones, we recalled to one another that, after all, our expedition was supposed to be a marine one, and took to the water.

Guatulco proved an unsatisfactory place because our captures were so sporadic and uncertain. Three hours of hard work with seine, bang-bang, or helmet might yield almost nothing of particular value, and then some delectable specimen would fairly swim into net or jar, and force its capture upon us. The water of this bay was exceedingly cold and made our helmet dives short and chilly. We tried out wire fish traps for the first time in the Pacific, variously baited, and with good success. But here, too, luck occasionally failed us, for a trap left overnight would sometimes contain nothing but a great, mud-colored moray eel of Falstaffian proportions. The second time this happened I became suspicious and dissected him. In his capacious stomach I found not only all our bait but the distinctly recognizable remains of ten fish, any of which, unswallowed, would have been a prize. After that Red Ridinghood experience, we pulled our traps up at shorter intervals.

One of the small beachlets of Guatulco had a real coral reef, the first we had seen deserving of the name, some distance off shore. It was roughly about fifty by two hundred yards, and some thirty from the beach. Like the semidesert landscape, it was not a pukka coral reef in the tropical sense of the word, the heads being low and the branches brown, two to six inches in length, and crowded close together. Small serranids and eels loved it, and many other fish which fled at the first hint of disturbance. We sent the boats and the huskier members of the crew to the reef with orders to bring as much as possible of it back. By pushing pails and tubs beneath the heads, they were pried off and lifted on board with a minimum loss of the inhabitants. The northern character was still apparent in the make-up of animal life, and many groups, such as serpent stars, worms, and mollusks, which, in a tropical reef, should have been present in great numbers and brilliancy were scarce.

On the deck we squatted Hinduwise, and with hammer and chisel attacked the unlovely masses of coral. Baby rockfish and demoiselles, and strange, slippery brotulids slithered out, while small sea cucumbers twisted about in the low-geared activity which Nature has vouchsafed them.

The dominant tenants were small red crabs and equally diminutive snapping shrimps. Wholly unlike one another in general shape, they yet were absurdly similar in color and pattern and certain reactions. They varied from a rich ferruginous red to a dark pink, and when seen deep within the interstices of the branches, they appeared identical. The tips of the big claws were black. Both became terribly excited at being chivied about their erstwhile quiet domicile, and at the first hint of trouble all slid down into the deepest crevices of the coral, like firemen sliding down their pole on a sudden alarm. The crabs and shrimps were both suited perfectly to this performance, but, spatially speaking, in diametrically opposite ways. The crabs were excessively *flattened*, thus enabling them to go sideways down a crack of smallest caliber, while the shrimps were correspondingly *compressed*, both body and claw, so that they followed the crabs, but tail first, around the close, irregular coral columns and stairways. If by chance they reached a cul-de-sac together, a fight promptly ensued, each apparently blaming the other for all this unprecedented upheaval of their cosmos. If epithets flew, the shrimps would certainly be saying, "You miserable blighters, you *Trapezia cymodoce ferruginea!*" And the crabs must of necessity answer, "Same to you, you sons of *Crangon ventrosus,* you!"

As a matter of fact, lacking vocal ejaculations, the shrimps can still express their emotions aloud, and as their homes were invaded, a veritable crescendo of castanets, of sharp snaps and clicks, would arise, near and far, as they frantically snapped their chelae in horror or in despair.

When I had broken through to their last retreat, with backs against the marble wall this thin red line of brave little crustaceans surrendered first their huge black-tipped claws, one after another. The shrimps then let go, and hurled themselves down to whatever lay below. If this happened to be the water in the tub, they swam swiftly away, but if they fell on deck, they lay helpless on the flat, dry surface, faintly clicking their requiem.

The crabs, on the contrary, when exposed beyond peradventure of further concealment, clung like grim death with all eight legs, fencing the approaching forceps with wildly waving claws, holding on even after these had been sacrificed. If they fell on deck, they scurried like mad for the scuppers, and flung themselves overside. This probably was a fatal act, with only the result, of problematical satisfaction to them, of expiring in their native element. The chance of a morsel of such conspicuous edibility running the vertical gantlet of all the voracious fish beneath our keel, before reaching safety within another coral reef, was indeed slender.

Our chart — testament, guide, friend, hope — showed that at Guatulco we were in the first of three baylets, so after another skirmish with sand flies which turned at once into a rout for us, we circled the next outjutting point of land and entered the haven of Santa Cruz Bay. But the governing noun was a misnomer, and the chart was wrong or the bay had shifted, for there was no protection from the sheer Pacific. Nevertheless, we allowed ourselves to be washed ashore on the great, lazy swells.

A single hut with overturned dugout and cracked paddles marked where a Mexican family — apparently the First, the Last, and the Only Family of Santa Cruz — had fled either from sand flies or to some Guatulcan *fiesta*. A dark spot far down the beach resolved through the binoculars into a forlorn, emaciated dog, seated on the sand, gazing miserably out to sea, and now and then raising its muzzle to high heaven and howling with prolonged but absolutely silent emotion.

Passing an enormous weed-hung rock well out from the shore, we followed an impulse and flopped overboard for a swim. The swells lulled us, gently lifting and lowering our floating selves. Then I thought, for no reason at all, that I would seize the right moment, let my feet reach the side of the rock, and kick myself far out. Just as I paddled myself into position, the mother of all swells came along, swung me up to the level of the very summit, and then sucked me down, down, exposing a great, solid, horrid zone of long-spined sea urchins. Against these, except for the sudden exposure, I should have joyfully kicked and been laid up for weeks unknown. This was about enough, and we all scrambled and fell over the gunwales and shouted the nautical equivalent of, "Home, James!"

But Santa Cruz had one more ace up her sleeve. Word had gone overland from Guatulco that the owner and staff on the *Zaca* were toothsome morsels, and off on the gentle evening breeze, together with the faint scent of acacias, came patrolling squadrons of sand flies. We could neither see nor hear them, but the sense of feeling was still strong in spite of our Guatulco battle scars.

Whenever I desire to conjure up a picture of supreme dismalness, I recall the scene of a deserted dog, seated in the exact center of a waste of sand, howling silently to itself and to the sea, on a lonely beach of Santa Cruz.

CHAPTER 14

Salvador—De Omnibus Rebus

WHEN we alleged civilized folk desert our cities and go to far, clean, open lands, there is much that we have to shed or molt or discard. We might even begin with the silly, unnecessary odds and ends of clothing, for when we get down to sneakers, shorts, a shirt, and occasionally a hat, we have acquired a comfort and freedom which no collar, tie, or trousers ever confer. As our nostrils are gradually purged of nicotine, leather, gasoline, smoke, and other man-made odors, a whole new world of delectable smells becomes manifest, and we can sniff and ecstatically wrinkle our noses in a new and precious code of etiquette of the sea and the jungle. All this is even more true of mental quirks. Reared as we are on atlases and maps, it is always a shock to pass from one country to another and find that after all one is not purple and the other orange.

For weeks we had been coasting along the western shore of Mexico, poking our bow into every likely-looking bay. Now, when we left Tangola, we sailed southward as fast as possible across the Gulf of Tehuantepec. The following day we watched an endless line of lovely, lofty sierras, almost too high and symmetrical for reality. The glass showed a cluster of houses which was Champerico, and suddenly we realized that Guatemala was slipping past and would be for us only a line of great mountains and a cluster of red roofs. Then, for a subconscious moment, came the small-boy wonder and a renewed examination through binoculars for something un-Mexican and pro-Guatemalan. All the geography colors of our youth were washed out. Even the ocean life — skipjacks, mackerel, flying fish, shearwaters, and dolphins — all were the same as off Mexico. One thing, however, Guatemala offered which I shall never forget — the superb volcano of Santa Maria, with a side shoulder pouring forth white smoke. Slowly, quietly, eternally, the cloud which was not a cloud wound upward. Like the old smoke language of the Navajo Indians, this new land had signaled me, "Look! I *am* different!" and I grinned and said, "Thanks," and liked Guatemala.

On the morning of the thirteenth of December, both Stormy Pete, our grand captain, and his chart insisted that the same old coast line was now still another country, Salvador. To me this stood only for a page of stamps in an album. I do not want to convey the idea that we leaped from Mexico to Salvador because of fear of fierce Tehuantepecker storms. Our route was controlled for the most part by bays, and Guatemala's coast seemed too smooth and even, on the chart, to suggest good shelter and collecting.

We had to stop at El Salvador's port of La Libertad to wait for the arrival of the *Santa Rosa* with mail, frozen meat, and other supplies, otherwise we should have missed seeing some lovely, some shocking, and some unexpected things. Anchoring off the port, we found it, geographically, the kind of place we should never have visited had it not been for the demands of our iceboxes. But before we left Salvador, we blessed that lack.

I found a small volume in the captain's cabin called *The Commercial Travelers' Guide to Latin America,* and from it I acquired a most amazing amount of useless jumbled information. "Salvador," I read, "is the most densely populated of Latin countries, with 109 inhabitants per square mile." Hearing a flood of Spanish, I looked up and saw a launchful of pompous little Salvadorian officials alongside. In fact, there were exactly eleven of them, so that somewhere one tenth of a square mile on shore had been depopulated (according to my Latin guidebook).

The poor dears were overdressed, buttoned much too tightly, so full of dignity that even the low bulwark was an effort, ultrapolite, with many asides, some of which I could understand. I once had a little monkey who tortured himself for no reason at all by often looking up into the trees, or into the far distance, when he was dying to touch or examine or eat something within reach, but completely self-conscious because of my presence. The sad, rusty pier and the sadder shore held much of the attention of our visitors when they were bursting to concentrate on the yacht and our scientific gadgets. It was the last word in inferiority complex. But two or three short, quick, strong ones refocused their whole beings. They unbuttoned themselves, physically and mentally; they pored over everything; they filled the air with hissing Spanish epithets of admiration. Thus by the judicious application of a moderate quantity of C_2H_5OH, the status of uncomfortable alien visitors had changed to that of friendly buddies. How great is chemistry!

When at last they saw our collections of fish in the laboratory, they broke loose in the universal language of anglers. Faster and faster came the spate of Spanish until all separation into words ceased. The last shred of translation passed from me and yet the gist of it all was, "Wedon'tcallthatalargeoneinSalvador!" Finally they signed our papers with happy flourishes, and most reluctantly they allowed the tenth of some square mile on shore to swallow them again. They were all grand *hombres*.

To say that La Libertad was an open roadstead is an understatement. From a horizon-long stretch of sand and straggly growth a spindly-legged steel pier reached far out toward us through an incredible number of breakers. The chief exports (so said my book) are "coffee, sugar, balsam, indigo, hats, honey, and hides." Being Commercial Travelers neither in honey, hides, nor hats, no machinery was set in motion for us, and we scrambled and clutched our way, as best we could, into Salvador. For the purchasers of indigo and balsam a little double seat is usually swung out to the boat by a crane. We had to brace ourselves and balance carefully as successive swells raised us six feet to heaven and then dropped us a fathom down toward the bottom of the sea. At the moment of greatest ascension we seized any reachable rung of a slippery iron ladder, and forthwith scuttled up out of the way. Our carcinologist almost came to grief because an extremely rare crab chose this moment out of all time to walk across an adjacent pile, and it took all our cries in English, and an equal but shriller volume in Spanish, to persuade her to let the crab go and preserve her life.

We walked down the pier with dozens of great swells rolling past, finally to break on the black lava sand. We watched with fascinated interest the Thursday ablutions of the Libertadian women and children, the former being clad in awful, full-length, calico gowns. The process consisted in rushing full speed down to the edge of the last receding wave, scooping up a gourdful of water-*cum*-sand, pouring it inside the front of the bedraggled wrappers or over the heads of the infants, and then fleeing for safety far up the beach. This was repeated until apparently complete exhaustion put an end. In this way modesty was achieved a full one hundred per cent, but cleanliness I should be inclined to rate at about a tenth.

We walked through the hot silent streets of the noontime siesta. From what we could see, the natives must be pitifully poor, and we marveled at the multiplicity of tiny shops and boxlike stores. Everyone must live by selling minute quantities of things to everyone else. Yet there were grilles set in adobe windows, even when the front door was broken beyond repair; an infinitesimal promenade and plaza had a floorless bandstand, with jungle plants pushing up and elbowing aside the bulbless electric fixtures. The grackles and ground doves alone seemed to benefit by the general deterioration. Earthquakes had frolicked with the pavement, and the attention of the usual evening parade of men and girls must often have been diverted from flirtation to watching their step.

To us, dining on the deck of the *Zaca*, the evening was sheer glory, a succession of pageants: first, a magnificent sunset with the afterglow from that red-hot sun setting fire to the cold clouds hanging over La Libertad; later, far away, from some active volcano, there arose the dull glow of unquenched fires of earth; and lastly there floated overhead the almost full moon, glowing but quite dead.

Early on the seventeenth day of December we donned unaccustomed clothing and again climbed the pier. A station wagon, so ancient that it gave us a feeling of complete security, awaited us, and we started for San Salvador, the capital of El or just Salvador. Our backbones soon vibrated in rhythm with Mr. Ford's conveyance, and the scenery became ever more and more splendid. We climbed and climbed, skirting the knife-edge summits of spurs, arroyos, and barrancas. Soon we had a distant and last view of the sea, doing a sort of reverse Balboa, and the majestic sierras fairly walked toward us.

The blobs of mud huts, scattered here and there, were each encased in a glory of bougainvillaea and poinsettia run riot. For many miles every speck of level or reasonably oblique ground was covered with coffee or maize. The huts were so few that I expected, sooner or later, to see a place where the native mestizos were standing shoulder to shoulder, to balance my book's estimate of "109 per square mile." Our driver was enthusiastic about side trips for which we had no time. When he suggested turning aside to visit a place called *Zacatecoluca*, we thought he was being funny in English slang, or that it was some place which would afford another view of the sea, far behind us, and the yacht, until we suddenly realized he was still talking Spanish and referred to a populous town which (my book again) "was hardly worth a visit by Commercial Travelers."

Houses improved and soon we passed estates, lovely with flowers, country clubs, and golf links. The overhanging volcano of Salvador rose higher as we approached its base, calm now, although it had broken forth and destroyed the city less than twenty-five years before. An attractive lake has gradually formed near its slopes, and the driver told us that very soon this must be dynamited and drained, since its increasing weight would result in terrible earthquakes. This was verified later by a geologist whom we met. On the farther side of the city was a smaller peak, raising its head, dusty and quiescent, which only a year before meted out death to ten thousand people near its base. Several times a day I am sure we all looked up rather apprehensively at these splendid peaks, but no native seemed ever to give them a thought.

At last we entered the narrow streets of San Salvador and engaged enormous cool rooms at the Hotel Nuevo Mundo. Our driver still hung around, chagrined at our disappointment at seeing so little bird life on the way. Suddenly his eye brightened, and he begged us to come and see "*todos los pájaros de Salvador, muy cerca.*" So we went a few blocks to find our objective, a little bird store with a few miserable tanagers and mockers. There were, however, two lovely solitaires, one beginning to whisper his incomparable notes beneath his breath.

Our next drive was to the Museo Nacional. This was housed in two large rooms connected by an outdoor covered passageway. To reach it we had to dispute the right of way with most friendly and affectionate burros and cows. The outdoor space was apparently the Zoo Nacional, as it was filled with a few old wire cages with white rats, guinea pigs, and rabbits, together with a pair of despondent spider monkeys, a caracara, and a raven. One of the monkeys was working with thumbless futility at a loose nail in its wire.

The natural-history room was partly blocked at the entrance by a case containing a double-headed calf, mounted, or, rather, stuffed, in a confusion of bodies and legs which defied understanding. At the sides of the room and down the center were small cases, literally falling apart and indescribably dusty. The entomological collection consisted of about one hundred butterflies which had been mounted in plant presses, for their bodies were as flat as their wings. The only lepidoptera which were thriving were the clothes moths which were having a grand time with the remains. The central case contained a pelican with pouch so distended with straw that it almost obscured the rest of the bird. A moth-eaten canary was half falling out of a nest made of cast-off cotton threads, while her eyeless spouse clung hopelessly to a wire branch above, defying all the laws of gravitation and of ornithological anatomy.

In the wall cases were several hundred abominably made bird skins, hung by their feet. Some, beneath the dust, were just recognizable as caciques and others as tanagers and herons; many were literally skins, with all the feathers in piles on the floor of the case. They were labeled, and in the absence of any guard and without much trouble I forced open a door and reached in. The labels bore nothing but the native name and a date; no collector or place. A few mastodon bones, molars and vertebrae, were almost coated with feathers which had dropped from the birds overhead.

A few Mayan idols, a lot of beautiful, black, obsidian arrow points, and some breastplates, spurs, and chests of the old conquistadores completed the museum. Last but not least was a railed-off, stained park bench on which an early president, his wife and daughter had been assassinated during a revolution.

We found out that the collection as a whole was the work of another president who had also been shot or stabbed about fifteen years before. Salvador has evidently been no place for a scientist. Like a few of our northern museums this of San Salvador was in the Stone Age of Science; it was almost worse than nothing. Let me add that no exaggeration has crept into this description. I have presented in accurate detail the Museo Nacional, and I have done this with the hope that soon Salvador will awaken to the wonders of her birds and beasts and butterflies of her forests and mountains. I would like to see added to her "coffee, sugar, balsam, indigo, honey, and hides" the interest to her own people and to visitors of a splendid zoo and museum. *Viva ciencia en Salvador!*

After a long walk through much of the city, three things were impressed upon us — we were the only tourists, thank heaven; there was a circus opening this very evening; and although the great day was a week away, the spirit of Christmas was rampant. In place of political and advertising posters were huge placards, *Viva Cristo Rey!* There were no beggars, and good manners characterized every class. Two little boys asked timidly if they could direct us anywhere, and in answer to my question one said that we must go to the telegraph office, have nothing to do with the operator, but ask for Jesús, who was the best guide there was. We agreed, and tipped him, but in the light of the full moon went our unregenerate way alone. Polite, considerate reporters interviewed us, and the following morning we found that even the stigma of *turistas* had been removed, and we had become *científicos*.

A few blocks from our hotel we sighted the exciting circus lights and tent top, but we almost regretted going in because every step thither was entertainment beyond price to our northern, Anglo-Saxon eyes. For the sum of seventy-five centavos we were admitted to the *palco*, which is Salvadorian for ringside seats, and our knees and toes were practically inside the twelve-inch red cloth which delimited the tanbark. A trapeze and tightrope nearly over our heads and a tiny ring made us settle down with contented sighs. There were no peanuts or pink lemonade, but delicious *cerveza* and *dulces*.

The audience in the bleachers numbered a hundred or more, mostly barefooted, bright-*rebozoed* peons and Indians, and quite a number of people in our reserved *palco*. There were two small, draped, board boxes, all on the bare earth, one of which was marked "Colonel Fachendoso." Soon the colonel and some family filed in, and looked at us aloofly as through lorgnettes. We didn't care for them and watched them hopefully, for we had seen a large tarantula creep over and into their box, and we longed for an unrehearsed act. But the spider had probably crawled into its hole in this erstwhile vacant lot, and the snooty ones had no scare.

Suddenly a whistle blew, and a splendid eight-man marimba band struck up within twenty feet of where we sat and played throughout the whole two hours plus of the performance, never too loud and often so softly that they formed a delightful obbligato to what was going on. *Rumba*, Sousa, overtures, Viennese waltzes, they played all uncommonly well. Behind us, several rows back, sat a man and a woman who were hardly real. She had huge features, made up beyond belief, and hair bleached blond with long dangling curls, and she was wholly unself-conscious, an exaggeration of Charley's Aunt. With her was a giant of a man with broken nose, scars everywhere, and a general cast of face as unbelievable as hers. We had a difficult time to keep from staring. They were like masks, caricatures of the worst-woman-in-the-world and the typical worst-bandit. Well-built but twice the size of the peons around them, they were perfectly well-behaved, laughing and applauding like children. Again it seemed as if it all was for our benefit, a Hollywood set inexcusably overdone, with us alive in the foreground.

Across the ring was an Indian family, the man with fine high nose and magnificent Mayan profile, the woman with hair to her waist, nursing a baby and wholly absorbed in everything that happened. The man who played the drums and other gadgets with such intricate and interchanging rhythm, as only a Latin American could, was another face never to be forgotten. As he drummed, or even when tapping and muting a cymbal, he looked off into space, completely engrossed, hypnotized. He had wide-flaring nostrils, high cheekbones, and infinitely sad eyes, combined with a strange, constantly searching, unfocused look, glancing everywhere in the intervals of playing, as if looking for something but dreading to find it. This sounds silly, melodramatic, and absurd, but we all separately sensed it. It was a face with fine and equally evil possibilities.

I was so interested in the marimba playing that I slowly drifted over, close to the players, and watched them before the show started. When they finished the first piece, I instinctively applauded heartily, as did we all, but no one else. We had very evidently made a Salvadorian social faux pas, but nevertheless the face of the drummer lit up amazingly with a smile, and then the mask settled down again. Near the entrance side of the *palco* the party of *correctos*, or well-to-do, people looked condescendingly about them at first, but afterwards broke down and enjoyed everything as much as anyone. Rather softly but consistently, after every special event, we clapped gently, and before the show was over, we had quite a claque who joined amateurishly in with us. Perhaps we established a new custom of audible appreciation in San Salvador.

A little boy in long trousers came out with a rush, looked around with what he pretended was astonishment, and bowed with what someone has called "pleased surprise" at sight of the audience. He was lifted up to a trapeze, and while a man stood beneath to catch him if he fell, he did some excellent balancing with and without a chair. Then a clown sang a very funny song with dozens of refrains, the humor of which evaded us entirely. In fact, all the high, or, rather, obviously low, comedy of the evening was tantalizingly nebulous to us, while the audience rocked. A slack-rope walker was surprisingly good, turning back somersaults. He and his long metal balancing pole were directly over my head, so I at first prayed for his skill, and later blessed it, as otherwise one *científico* would have been carried down to the coast on a shutter.

Came more clown and then a very lovely *señorita* in tights and spangles who sang a topical song to the delight of everyone including ourselves. After this a man changed water to rice before our eyes and made a pack of cards vanish with somewhat insufficient speed. Then several clowns with helpers, and a man and a boy with a wooden barrel. Father balanced and juggled the barrel on his feet as he lay on his back, and then cleverly juggled the boy. Finally two acrobats did as high trapeze as the tent permitted, after ten minutes of net stretching below. Once, when one man slipped, we could hear the gasp of breath as his partner let him fall. They too were really good, and the singing *señorita* was terribly worried about the one who fell.

Next came a rather sad little circus pinto pony and a black dog. The dog rode the horse as the horse jumped low sticks, and then, by dint of scraping him off the saddle blanket, the dog was made to seem to jump. When he failed, as he mostly did, the horrible woman who had the whip gave the assisting clown such a look as would have driven me to the mountains in terror of my life. We unanimously hated that woman.

Then the ever-pleasant *señorita* came out and danced a *rumba*, and all was well again. Finally the clowns, and all the company unsuccessfully disguised, joined in an intricate farce, linguistically far over our heads, but emotionally only too apparent, after which the giant Negro who moved the scenery rushed on with a flaming torch, chased all the actors and performers away, and everyone except ourselves knew that the circus was over. The moonlight and the pleasant Indian and edible smells outside and the glimpses through the doors into the patios made it all seem like life on another planet compared with ours on the *Zaca*.

My room, which was enormous and with a ceiling so high that it seemed as if stars ought to be shining above me, looked out on a plaza with a filling station and a stand for a dozen cars along the edge. I went to bed a little after midnight and listened for a while. At one o'clock a roaring arose like the beginning of a volcanic outbreak, soon changing into a whistling howl behind the hotel. Then came the squeal of brakes, toots for the filling-station man, half-tone double horns, cracked shrieks from broken calliopes — all this almost continuous. Then the church bells began for some untemporal reason, with seven or eight *gang! gang! gang!* then a rest, then seven or sometimes nine. It was like the Indian brain-fever bird, these bellbirds of Salvador. Having made up my mind to listen and enjoy it, I promptly went to sleep and did not waken until six o'clock. The sun leaped up and all the midnight pandemonium redoubled, with the addition of untold numbers of firecrackers in honor of the coming Christmas. The Salvadorians cannot have snow, but they can have gunpowder and they do. I counted eighteen kinds of automobile horns, between six and seven o'clock.

Then came burro-drawn carts with old frying pans hung beneath and stone clappers pounding against them, as guards against scorching automobiles. Wooden hammers of ice-cream vendors, and street cries running the gamut of the human vocal chords from rumbling bass to highest *c*'s. I shrieked in sympathy in the shower and could hardly hear myself, and then went down to a delicious breakfast.

We reveled in the markets all the morning. As I have said, we were the only tourists in the city, and nine tenths of the customers were Indians or peons with *cinco* centavos as the outside limit for any one purchase. So all the stocks in trade were geared to this economy. The result was to put to utter shame any five-and-ten-cent store ever conceived in northern marts. Christmas, only a week away, was the motive everywhere. Along the gutters of the streets bordering the markets were hundreds of small stalls, mostly without coverings, and with old newspapers or great leaves spread on the ground as counters and showcases. Here were thousands upon thousands of tiny clay images, all made by hand, from minute beings less than an inch long to three-foot dragonlike creatures born of untrammeled imaginations. There were women patting tortillas with dishes of most realistic edibles around, a woman with a machete killing a turkey, and hosts of single creatures, armadillos, guinea hens, vultures, squirrels, soldiers, clowns, saints, and washerwomen. All were made by Indians in the vicinity of San Vicente. Some were crude and hardly recognizable; a great many showed extreme beauty and anatomical knowledge, some slavishly representing every muscle, others fashioned in the most modernistic style.

Since all were handwork, no two were exactly alike. Most of the little figures were brightly painted and had practical stands, and the average price was five centavos, or two cents American. We began to buy and then realized we had no way of carrying them, so went into the market proper and purchased baskets of varied shapes and gorgeous patterns.

The dominant theme, as I have said, was Christmas and the materials of the cheapest. There were thousands of Christ childs, all pink, lying with a tiny bit of white cloth about their middles. Equal numbers of burros lay or even sat, together with cows and sheep, but no goats. Local color was occasionally introduced into the diminutive Noel crèches, and often in place of the attendant burros and cows, there were realistic spoonbills, zopilotes, and armadillos. It was easy to visualize and excuse the workings of the Indian mind which fashioned these sweet little tableaux, in unconsciously populating the villages of Palestine with unmistakable Neotropical fauna. The owner of one stall was attempting to establish a new motif in manger decorations, and in these the Christ child looked up at a background of colored pages from Sears, Roebuck or Stumpp & Walter catalogues, while batlike birds of flaming red hovered on wires over the heads of the Holy Family. In the mind of this artist there appeared to exist a certain confusion between Santa Claus and the virgin birth, because in a dozen tableaux an obvious Santa in white beard and red jacket looked benignly down on the manger. Here, too, was the only attempt at cottony snow, which must have been incomprehensible to most of the Indian onlookers, and the presence of which in the Bethlehem stable carried a suspicion of hyperbole.

The allegories were fascinating: the devil in black and gold pushing a woman, apparently not too unwilling; another fiend holding a ball of gold with silver circles on it representing filthy lucre; still another with spread bat wings clutching a diminutive bottle, with at least two dozen more bottles strewing the ground.

We bought recklessly, and returned again and again, so that the people got to recognize us and rushed off to get new things to tempt the millionaire scientists who apparently possessed endless numbers of *cinco* centavos. One booth had piles of sections of huge posters, incomplete sheets of well-known cigarette brands, or the lower right-side quarter of Greta Garbo's face. These were selling briskly, probably intended for wallpaper in distant huts.

The market proper seemed to go on and on for miles, with hundreds of stalls with baskets, *rebozos*, flowers, real and artificial, woven cloths of great beauty from Guatemala, saddles giving forth delicious leather smells, shoes, and a central court with immense piles of earthenware vases, ollas, jars, and dishes. Unless we were very vigilant, we would almost step on the tiniest of tiny babies crawling nakedly about on their occasions, and when we left a basket for a few minutes, we would look carefully inside to make sure that no infant was curled up asleep. Vegetable, meat, fish, grain, all had piles of very small cornucopias with single vegetables, and almost countable grains, for the inevitable *cinco* centavos.

We watched an Indian family buying a small Christ, and for minute after minute the talk would go on, the choice wavering between a very small one with a burro couchant, or a larger, pinker one alone. Toward the end I had an admiring crowd following me, watching the treasures go into my great baskets. I staged an exciting scene over a little tableau of seven zopilotes, or vultures, red heads and all, on a paper and wire tree, all wriggling delightfully on their individual wires, while on the ground below was a blotch and mound of something awful in bright yellow with purple spots. I demanded to know on what the vultures were feeding before I would purchase. "*Quécomen los zopilotes?*" I asked, and the whole street giggled. People collected. A truckman blew his horn, but no one paid any attention, so he climbed down, elbowed in, and giggled with the rest. At last the girl owner answered, "*Muertos.*" This would not do as I demanded what *muertos*? Someone prompted, "*Carne.*" I tentatively suggested, "*Hombre?*" but this brought down a whole chorus of, "*No, no, señor; nunca hombre!*" with a note of seriousness threatened, so I acquiesced, and at last an urchin screamed, "*Perro!*" After a long discussion in which at least ten persons joined, we all agreed that *perro* was right and I made the purchase, I think to everyone's regret because it put an end to this excitement.

CHAPTER 15
Papagayo Paradise

THERE is a bay where I should like to spend a full year, through all the seasons, watching the shift and change underwater, along the shore, in mangroves, palm and thorn forest, and upland grass meadows. One of our first trips took us up through lush mangroves, the tide carrying us along ever-narrowing channels, until we pushed our way by hand into ultimate water paths, flushing curlews, bitterns, herons, and kingfishers. Dry land appeared and we climbed up into an enchanted forest, or, rather, park, of lofty trees where bands of spider monkeys swung by their tails, apparently exchanging pointed remarks on how queer human beings looked upside down. One lot of three females were all carrying babies, and in all the pram method was identical. The baby had its tail tightly wrapped around the base of its mother's tail, as it lay on her back, with its little arms around her mid-body, gripping the hair on the lower sides. The hind legs lay straight out behind, with the black soles up, dangling close to the haunch of the mother. In this way the limbs and tail of the parent were quite free, and the baby safe from any sudden danger of being crushed when the mother dropped from one branch or tree to another with widespread limbs. When the parents sat down and looked at us, the little chaps would pull themselves up, and each black face peered at us alongside that of its mummy.

Here I observed what later became a common occurrence, that all the members of the band followed one another, and took exactly the same path through the trees. Each took hold of the identical same part of the same branch as the one ahead, leaped free at the same spot, and used the hands at the same place. Arboreal safari for spider monkeys is as fixed as a well-worn trail through thick undergrowth.

The grass, the meandering streams, the enormous wide-spreading trees might all have been in an English park, instead of a Pacific wilderness of Costa Rica. But a pair of loud-voiced macaws and the swooping flight of trogons, together with the fresh tracks of tapirs, refocused our latitude. Following the stream, we came to more open country with deep, sandy cuts and piles of dry logs and debris, showing the terrific power of the water in the rains. The logs were now covered with orchids in flower and a swarm of butterflies and equally brilliant lizards. I watched three very different butterflies alight on a mighty prostrate log, and all, at the same moment, vanished. The first invariably lit in the midst of foliage, and its patterned network of brown and black lines made it a leaf among leaves; a morpho dazzled the eye with its blazing blue, but when its feet touched the bark, the wings snapped together and the eye, still blue conscious, lost the insect completely. The third was a medley of bluish white and gray, and swooped swiftly to the bark, becoming on the instant only another flake, with the wings pressed flat, so that not a hint of telltale shadow should escape. I greeted my very special *Junonia coenia*, and watched a five-inch jungle dragonfly float slowly past, with its greenish-yellow spots apparently pinwheeling through the air in dizzy spirals.

A quarter mile farther and the stream abruptly sank into the sand, and facing us were seven large and capable-looking bulls. For a moment all watched us with outstretched muzzles, and my heart almost stopped, because from past experiences in the Malay States and India I am more afraid of seladangs and water buffalo than of any other living creature. But after what seemed hours, these turned about, and with the dainty, mincing trot of wild cattle, they left the arroyo. From time to time the stream put forth a pool and then ducked out of sight again, and these isolated bits of water, although as nearly fresh as might be, contained gobies, pipefish, clingfish, and mullets.

Another day we landed on the opposite shore, frightening vultures from the carcass of a fourteen-foot crocodile. Around and beneath it were hundreds upon hundreds of hermit crabs, their shells clashing and tinkling pleasantly as they pushed and climbed upon the horrid feast. Above the beach line we cut and crawled through solid thickets, with bitterns and small crocs for audience, and once a tapir sloshed in person through the mud to some lair unreachable by us. We climbed through bull's-horn thorn bushes, each thorn with a cohort of fire ants. To an observer our actions could have been only comic, as we skirted gingerly each innocuous-looking bush, and politely lifted aside every branch so as not to awaken the concealed ants.

We climbed and climbed until we entered upland meadows, and suddenly six cowboys rode across our path, herding wild horses, en route to a distant ranchero. Up and along sharp ridges we went on, following vague trails which, as in the Himalayas, always ran along the very crests. The bay came into view with the *Zaca* at anchor, the distant Pacific breakers, volcanoes with their tops swathed in cloud; and as we looked down, a pair of macaws flew past, their backs, tails, and wings ablaze with scarlet, blue, and yellow. Always overhead swung the zopilotes, the watchful, hopeful, graceful vultures, and still higher, mere motes against the blue, frigate birds observed the whole world stretched out beneath them. Throughout all this day the Papagayo had miraculously died down. Only a soft breeze blew, although we could see cat's-paws stepping across the water, and far away a waterspout pirouetted as it drifted.

The hardest collecting at El Canelo was along a coral isthmus, near the outer end of the bay, an isthmus which connected the mainland with a single, gigantic, rocky islet. At low tide there was never less than a foot of water over the coral, yet we were able to scatter our derris-root poison to windward, and then collect frantically as the slow current carried half-stupefied octopi, worms, and all manner of strange fish toward us. Papagayo, with Force Three, never let up a moment, and when the tide and waves threatened to wash us out to sea, we were staggering with weariness, completely salt-encrusted, but happy with pailfuls of rare, brilliant eels and interesting young stages of angelfish, and even baby sharks and rays. The coral itself defeated us until, one morning, I pushed a full stick of dynamite as far down as possible. We all took what shelter we could find behind most inadequately small boulders, and detonated it. The geyser which rose high in air was filled with coral, the wind gave it impetus, and for many seconds we were cruelly bombed by sharp pieces. But the bruises were worthwhile, for this method routed out fish which had so far defied all our efforts. Long after we returned to the *Zaca*, we found ourselves instinctively bracing against the blasts which had harassed us all day, giving our muscles no respite.

The value of a variety of methods in studying the fishes of these bays was shown by a comparison of tide-pooling, seining, and bongbonging (i.e., dynamiting) in the course of one half of one day. In the tide pools we took 65 fish of 6 species; in seining we hauled

416 fish of 17 kinds; in bong-bonging 186 fish yielded 15 species. But of these different species of fish, taken in three ways, only 2 were duplicated, so unlike were the results of the several methods.

We had come to this bay to learn what we could of its fishes, and we had captured a splendid lot, from fresh-water mullet and clingfish out of isolated pools, a mile up a dry arroyo, to wholly new frogfish from the depths of the outer coral reefs. On the morning of the eighteenth of January I landed on East Beach (*Zaca* nomenclature), a beach of pebbles, shady trees, and hermit crabs, and settled for a careful survey of the bay. I knew there were schools of fry everywhere; we had bong-bonged with small caps and netted thousands. But what was still a mystery were the hosts of fry-eaters, fish about a foot in length which leaped in every direction, but which thus far had evaded all efforts at capture. Now and then one jumped wholly out of the water, and I hoped to be able to catch a clear glimpse of it through glasses. In the space of two hours of intermittent watching, I had three definite chances, although the necessity for instantaneous refocusing of one's eyes as the silvery form appeared for a moment through the binoculars was the devil's own trouble. But something more than deliberate recognition registered, and I knew for certain that the fry-eaters of Port Parker were cousins of bonefish and tarpon, fish of solid silver, with the silliest name in fishdom — Tenpounders! And with them were several small jacks whose leaps gave me the chance of naming them a hundred yards away. This provided the facts I wanted, and showed that by patience we could identify other species than flying fish in mid-air. We had taken both fish in the vicinity of the fry, but their empty stomachs made them worthless proofs. A postscript to this day's observations was that two days later, after my prolonged and successful vigil, we seined both species bursting with great meals of the selfsame fry.

A second problem was the succession of fish advancing in from the sea with each tide: which came first, and why. This was easier, for from a mangrove perch, looking down into the clear water throughout several tides, I got exactly what I wanted.

The phrase "intermittent watching" which I have used is only too real. As a scientist, I suffer from the limitations of generalities, with all the faults and unspeakable joys of the older naturalists. Until I was allowed to possess a gun, I was botanist and entomologist of sorts; then I became ornithologist for the greater part of my life; and in the last decade I have turned ichthyologist. These are all lip services, however, for the underlying urge is to glimpse some small, clear gleam in the workings of evolution in some sub-subdivision of an insignificant bypath of animal life and development. So it was that in the intervals between actually straining every effort to solve the day's two fish problems, I was acutely conscious of the general life of this lovely bay.

My two assistants had left me, one on a sketching assignment, and the other to delve into the intimate life of the fiddler crabs among the mud flats farther along the shore. I settled down between two giant black mangrove trees, one of which was hollow and wind- and age-worn. I made camp by opening my dispatch case of glasses, notebooks, and vials, scooped two holes in the sand for my heels, and sat down on a life preserver filched from the boat. This precaution was out of respect for the bêtes rouges, those infinitesimal mites which seem to be among the most successful of living creatures, sustained by the ultimate nth-power hope of being able to feast upon a human being before they die. I have found them equally enthusiastic on the tennis courts of Virginia as in the tropical jungles of British Guiana, and here on the shores of the Pacific they teemed, from the grass of the upland meadows to the very jetsam of high-tide line.

As my job today was static, I allowed myself the luxury of two pairs of glasses, my smallest Number 3's for nearby use and quick identification, and the powerful Number 12's which required knee rest, for distance. In addition to my two grand mangroves was a third, a whitened, dead tree. Hardly had I taken my seat when a sonorous swish of wings drew my eyes upward and out flew a great blue heron whose spindly frame and immobility had up to this moment made him one with the tree. As I looked, two black hawks flew into the same tree, the common white-banded black species. They were handsome birds and peered at me fearlessly, uttering pleasantly quavering hawk notes. An interesting thing about birds of prey is the possibility of prophesying the diet of a species from its psychological reaction to human beings. At one end are the vultures, which are almost completely fearless. At the other are the fierce falcons and eagles, which pursue and kill their prey, diving after the strongest and swiftest creatures they can manage. These black hawks have the noble facies of gerfalcons, but their all too tameness hints that, gastronomically, they are among the ignoble *raptores*, satisfied at the most with small lizards, but usually content with grasshoppers, snails, crabs, and even dead fish. There is nothing vulturine in their mien, but their ease in the presence of mankind is a certain proof that no black hawk ever struck down a flying duck, or any bird near its own weight. By the same token, bald eagles are far less wild than are golden eagles.

After the hawks had fled, I had several moments of absolute quiet. Then a familiar sound focused my senses on the shore, where a spotted sandpiper was watching me, teetering with polite inquiry, but considering me too slight a danger to interrupt for long its feeding. No matter how strange the locality, in spite of parrakeets screeching in the distance, first impressions dominate later experiences, and the *peep-sweet* of this little shore bird was always sufficient to overlay all this tropical environment and replace it with the millpond in New England where I first saw and identified the bird. It scampered on out of sight, and presently there came a jolly cackling, a familiar-unfamiliar sound, and the sandpiper had run into a pair of scarlet-billed oyster catchers, who were telling him impolite things in *Haemantopus* language.

Fish again absorbed me, until two blurred objects on the shore came into focus with a twist of the binocular thread. A pair of sandpipers this time, one with a primary feather reversed, standing straight up from the wing and waving in the breeze. I watched them idly as they passed on, when suddenly there took place, within the small circle of the lens, a happening that brought me to breathless attention. The little chap with the half-molted feather was suddenly knocked off his feet into a fluttering heap. Discarding the glass, I saw the whole tragedy clearly. A black log, stranded by the water's edge, had suddenly come to life, shifting from dead vegetable to living animal, and with a single, unbelievably swift, sideways flick of the tail had knocked the sandpiper over. As I looked, the head turned, the jaws opened, and a four-foot crocodile sank from sight with the pitiful fluff of feathers. I watched the rising stream of bubbles, I listened to the agonizing *peeeep-peeeep!* of the other bird and the shrieking cackles of the oyster catchers until all were lost in the distance. The only remaining proof of what my eyes had seen was that there remained only one instead of two logs. I immediately focused on the second to make certain it was what it appeared to be. During the past two days I had watched small crocodiles floating past, but the movement plus the two bulging eyes identified them at once. This stranded individual had completely fooled two sandpipers and myself.

The only bird sound from the jungle behind me was a resonant double note, repeated at long intervals, and occasionally answered in the distance two notes higher. These were telegraph tom-toms of great black and white ivory-billed woodpeckers. They had at least four drums, hollowed by lightning and seasoned by sun and rain. These rat-tat-tats kept up a pleasant, subdued, antiphonal obligato throughout all the afternoon, soon, like Dunsany's cricket, merging into the silence.

A medley of voices arose not long after the sandpiper tragedy, and as it did not die down, I walked quietly along the inland trail. Just beyond the uprooted base of a giant tree, I saw a flock of birds and simultaneously felt a sharp bite on my ankle. I had stepped into the line of march of army ants, and as instantly I stepped out again. The reason for the flock now became apparent; they were the camp-following vanguard feeding on the insects which crept, ran, hopped, or flew to escape their dreaded enemy. I found a convenient dead branch and as quietly as possible drew it back and forth across the trail of the ants. I knew that this would so infuriate them that they would deploy in search of the creature which dared disturb them, and this would keep them, and consequently the birds, in the same place for some time. I sought safety and settled to watch. There were four kinds of ant birds and a surprising lot of orioles. Three troupials fluttered about after insects, alternating satisfied swallows with clusters of liquid notes. A black-throated oriole flew down close to me, and then suddenly I was glad to see a friend from home, a Baltimore oriole among these alien surroundings. What tales migrants such as this and the sandpipers had to tell their nestlings! No wonder each season's brood is so anxious to set out on its autumnal, austral voyage of discovery! (Anthropomorphic, all anthropomorphic!)

Finally, six rich rufous beauties scaled down to the ant-driven harvest — rufous cuckoos. They measured more than a half yard over all, and their exciting loveliness of plumage, with the long, trailing, white-tipped tail made them most conspicuous birds. Their unusual size and general coloration always recalled female curassows. Yet the latter, with all their strength and stout beaks, are the most timorous of jungle birds, whereas these cuckoos, with beak and claws of the weakest, flaunt their brightness with utmost carelessness. They must have some way, of which we are wholly ignorant, of escaping the abundant hawks. They saw me at once but showed only polite curiosity, now and then uttering their low, soft snarl, which is in no sense a snarl, but lacks any adequate expression in the English tongue. They flew gently, gliding whenever possible, and fed gently, daintily selecting small morsels with no sense of hunger or haste, but somewhat reluctantly, like the oyster-eating carpenter.

I was squatting quite motionless, and comfortable, having only, now and then, to wink. So one cuckoo relegated me to the background of innocuous growth, and, alighting on a partly bare branch, proceeded to take a sun bath. The plumage is so soft and silky that it would seem as if the water or dust bath to which most birds are addicted would leave it with permanently bedraggled feathers. This sun bathing was as elaborate as it has become among human beings, but was infinitely more artistic and pleasing to observe. The bird first sat still and looked in all directions, complimenting me by concentrating on the branches overhead and the sky. It suddenly struck a pose, legs apart, leaning backward, slanting the great tail and spreading it until it formed a gorgeous open feathered fan, curved so that the white tips showed from both sides. The wing on the slanted side followed, and was expanded until, like the Argus pheasant, it presented a flattened plaque. Always the eye of the bird played back and forth across the sky; at least at such a period of toilet-making, a realization of possible danger was evident.

Slowly the feathers of the head and neck were raised (through my lenses I could distinguish every separate plume), until all beauty of color was lost, and the plaque acquired the appearance of moth-eaten plumage long neglected in some dusty attic. After a few minutes the bird began to pant, and to general dishevelment was added the impression of acute physical discomfort. Ten minutes, and all muscles relaxed, and the bird began to pick and preen its plumage, the intensive efforts hinting that ticks and *bêtes rouges* may afflict *Piaya cayana* as well as *Homo sapiens*. Not until a second bath was enjoyed by the other wing, with the tail re-slanted, did the bird shake its whole being, wipe its beak on the branch, and fly up into a mass of lavender flowers of cortez.

As I looked down, preparing to shift my stiff, tightly flexed limbs, I saw that a small spiny-bodied spider had stretched three strands of suspension cable from knee to knee, and I felt that I had really entered into the feeling of the jungle.

On my return to the shore, I once more settled down to a final hour of writing, when a tantalizing wheezy note arose from the tree overhead. I had to determine whether it was insect or bird, and my eye went at once to what looked like a small duck perched in a crotch. This spelled no sense whatever, yet amid the shadows of the foliage I could see bill, eye, and the head drawn close to the back. Two feet farther up I was startled to see the brilliant and unmistakable tail loop of a boa constrictor, and now I followed it down to the small duck, and the scales fell from my eyes and for the life of me I could not regain the anatine illusion; there was no duck, there had been no duck; only three loops of a beautifully colored serpent. In fact, the glasses showed that from the tangled mass of loops there projected two heads, one much larger than the other. I needed a boa for comparison with a strangely patterned specimen we had caught a few days before. A second would decide whether this unusual coloration was of specific or only individual signifi-cance.

The snake was twenty feet above me, on a dead branch which would not sustain my weight for a moment. I cut a long forked stick and began to jiggle him, which made him only grip the tighter. He began to creep slowly up the branch, when I got a good pur-chase with a recurved crook, and swinging on it, broke the whole branch, and down came a rain of rotten wood, debris, dust, and more than seven feet of snake. Fearing it would escape if it touched the ground, I blindly clutched at it in mid-air, and no lifelong-trained juggler could have done it better, for my fingers closed firmly around the neck just behind the head. Like all his kind, he gaped widely, uttering hiss after hiss, showing every needle tooth and an enormous expanse of dead white gullet, all the time trying with every muscle to coil and twist free. Then he gave up, and as boas are real gentlemen, he shrugged whatever pass for serpentine shoulders, and resigned himself to what might come. From this mo-ment on, there was no visible resentment, or active attempt to escape. The coils came slowly up and around my hand and arm, and when I had cleared the dirt from my eyes, I did not have to shift my grip a single inch.

I looked longingly up at the second boa, beautifully marked and at least twelve feet in length, but saw no way of getting him as he climbed to the very summit of the tree. An hour later when I again looked, he had vanished, although he must have reached out over a four-foot interval of thin air between the dead tree and the nearest live one.

Returning to my seat, I found neither string nor bag nor con-tainer, so that I had to shift my hold to the left hand to continue note writing with the right. My foot rested gently on the boa's tail on the sand, because with all his folds in a double lock on my wrist, he was able to stop the blood supply, and the hand ached too much to keep a tight grip. As it was, I had to stop writing every ten minutes, shift hands, and exercise to restore circulation. As the lowering sun struck his armor, he was one of the most beautiful things in the world, each scale giving off blue and green fire-opal reflections. Like the jumbled mass of leaf patterns and leaf shadows scattered along his body, his very eyes, lidless and unwinking, were also mottled with gray and brown, divided equally, while the vertical slit of visual connection with the outside world was almost invisible.

During one of the hand-to-hand shifts I happened to look out over the bay, and floating past was a pair of huge sea turtles, clasped in the awkward embrace of chelonian affection. I focused my glasses and perceived that it was a most active amorous episode, for not only were they excitedly clambering over and around one another, but both were revolving as they drifted past. First one arched back would emerge, decorated with clusters of barnacles, and then the other, gay with waving strands of emerald seaweed. Which sex flaunted the weed and which had acquired the barnacle insignia will never be known. This afternoon was rapidly becoming dominantly a reptilian one.

When I withdrew my eyes from the binoculars, I found myself securely handcuffed by two loops of boa, one of which was a figure eight. I saw the boatmen approaching, and did not untwine the snake until they had had full benefit of what to them seemed an incredibly terrible situation. They were strong, brave, able seamen, but I think if it came to a choice of unwinding the coils with their own hands, they would have left me marooned forever on the beach!

Subsequently the color comparison was made, the boa housed overnight on the yacht, and next day I set him free on the exact spot on which he would have fallen from the tree. He gathered himself together, watched me calmly, and finally, with exploratory flickering of his tongue, slowly made his way into the tangle of underbrush. From the opposite side I watched him glide smoothly along. Before he had passed from my actual field of vision, he vanished suddenly, from my inability to disentangle him from his surroundings.

The boa constrictor of East Beach had entered and had left my life; he none the worse, and I with added knowledge and respect for him and his race.

CHAPTER 16
Pacific Jungle

THE first evening at Golfito, when we went out on deck a little before seven for dinner, seemed unusually dark, and in a few minutes the rain, tropical rain, came down in torrents. It was the first of the whole trip, and it set all my long latent mental reactions into full play. Were the laboratory windows closed? (In my air-conditioned cabin there was only a single, sealed porthole!) What had been left out? (A glance around showed only several pairs of salt-encrusted sneakers, to which rain was a gift from heaven!) The rain fell as it can fall only in the tropics, straight and windless, then died out in a mist. I did not need the crepuscular voices of the tinamous and the giant toads from the shore to emphasize our latitude.

Early next morning the yelping of toucans excited us before we got halfway to shore. Winding through a shallow barrier of mangroves, we found a busy world of early feeders, herons, sandpipers, silver-beak tanagers, bright rufous squirrels (as unbelievable to a gray squirrel as a panda to a raccoon), and kiskadees. Then a black cat, like an elongate puma, flowed along the curved roots — a jaguarondi. As we landed, macaws and orchids complemented each other, equal in gorgeous colors, one shattering the air with startling cries, the other spraying perfume to such a distance that it was a miracle in the hot, breathless air.

"Why are the huge leaves of that vine filled with slots and holes?" asked our doctor. "That," said I, "is the hurricane plant, and after a great storm that vine will be the only thing left alive, because the force of the wind is broken by filtering through the openings — no, never mind writing it down; that's a joke; go pick up that wasp."

"One joke at a time is enough," retorted Eric. So I went over and picked up the wasp myself and handed it to my friend. It was wicked-looking, from the trembling, nervous antennae to the gauzy wings, the yellow bands on the abdomen, and the quivering, pointed sting. When we put the insect in a vial and examined it under a hand lens, the antennae were still more wasplike than anything else, but the wings, instead of being divided by an intricate network of horny lines, were reticulated by lines of minute scales; the head and body were not hard smooth armor, but covered with minute feathery scales, and the sting, instead of being an intricate poison apparatus, was a slender bundle of harmless hairs. But even this wasp impersonator could not quite alter the shape of its body and produce a suitable wasp waist; its guardian Master of Mimicry had dipped his brush in dark pigment, drawn a broad band of black shadow across the base of the abdomen, and behold! the wasp waist. Color, antennae, abdomen, wings, even every movement — a quick, jerky walk, a nervous curving around of the sting — all were those of a dangerous yellow jacket. Yet this insect came from a caterpillar, not a grub, and it was wholly and altogether a perfectly good moth.

The incredible marvel of this mimicry slowly filled Eric's consciousness, and I was glad that we both stood for a long time, looking and wondering in silence. Vocal exclamations are often only underappreciations. We were lucky to have this one of our first jungle finds, for it so aptly illustrated the terrific struggle for life here, compared with the easier tension among the lesser census of wild creatures of temperate and northern lands. Not a niche must be left unfilled, not a trick or artifice unattempted in the evolution of jungle existence.

The trail was rough but wide and fairly clear, and it was different from any other jungle trail I had ever seen — it was straight, impossibly straight. The explanation came later from a young American engineer who told us that it was the first rough survey line for a United Fruit narrow-gauge railway. It would some day receive bananas from great (present blueprint) plantations in Golfito and carry them straight through the jungle, over two low ranges, into the next bay to the south, which is in Panama. So the wonders of this jungle became all the more precious, because so soon they would be thinned out and frightened, and in place of great trees and lovely orchids and birds there would be men and dogs, bananas and pay days. Ultimately, some men, somewhere, would be able to deposit large sums of money in their banks, but they would never know or care how much more attractive and scenic were macaws and jungle lilies than chickens and miles of banana plants, how infinitely sweeter the voices of tinamous and wild pigeons than the barking of curs and the roar of outboard motors. But if I keep this up, I shall dissolve into sentimentality, and weep into my journal! So I shall return to Eric and the jungle as it was on this sixth day of March.

The first half mile along this trail showed all the typical characters of a tropical jungle. Whether in the lowlands of British Guiana, or the hinterland of Brazil, in the African Congo, the hot, steamy, leech-ridden forests of the Malay States and Borneo, or here, at sea level, on the coast of southern Costa Rica, the same general description applies. A few yards along the trail there loomed a tree trunk, yards around. The bark was utterly hidden beneath tassels of moss and mosaics of lichens. Up and up our eyes followed the mighty bole, straight and free from limbs, until high in space, yards and yards above the topmost twig of our northern forests, the first limbs appeared. Small insects, perhaps little butterflies, flew about up there, until our glasses changed them into goodsized birds. It was like looking down from a plane at the sea from a mile or more and suddenly having the distance made real by the lazy crawling of a tiny ship — actually a large freighter.

Twenty-five yards beyond the first great tree another appeared, this one smooth and clean, with graceful buttresses flowing, winding far out from the trunk, thin and soft-looking as the folds in a daguerreotype of our grandmother's bridal train. The tops of these jungle giants spread so wide, and intercepted so much sunshine, that only saplings and weaker growths could thrive between. The comparison of a jungle with a cathedral is often apt — the enormous bare columns, the quiet, the oblique colored shafts of light reaching through the lofty emerald sky windows down to the very floor. But the simile of cathedraled aisles may sometimes become confused, for abruptly, in the course of our walk, from the highest aerial foliage to the lowliest growths there appeared a network of streamers, vines, living strands and lianas, sometimes gay with orchids and air plants, often tangled and looped like the rigging of a wrecked ship.

Luck was with us, for soon we came to a place where the undeviating necessity of the trail had compelled the cutting straight through upper trunk and limbs of a mighty fallen tree. I could safely prophesy that here the curtain would go up for us on one of the most dramatic, affecting jungle episodes: the prologue, the smashing, catastrophic fall of the giant tree, with act succeeding act, scaled down to the patient, ultraslow-motion tempo of plant growth.

I led Eric down the long length of trunk, horizontal but poised on roots and branches ten feet above the ground. Finally we reached the great mass of upturned roots. The tree had fallen a few months before, and the wide clearing thus exposed to the sun had already begun its regular botanical evolution, that unvarying, so familiar sequence.

Almost like the quick reaction of a host of little animals, un-numbered tiny plants, daisylike, had awakened from their long seed sleep, flung wide their leaves, and burst into thousands of blossoms. We do not know how their seeds ever reached this place, or how long they had aestivated in the uncongenial dusk of the jungle floor. Now they were having their brief carnival of life, has-tening to ripen their seeds for another generation. But even as their petals fell, the second line of vegetation rushed into the unexpected gap, the small island of light in the dark sea of the jungle. This was an unlovely blitz, a tangle of low thorny vines, terrible saw-edged razor grass, soft-wooded, swift-growing spiny brush, forming che-vaux-de-frise wholly impenetrable to two- and four-legged creatures of any size.

But even on the day of the fall, other plants had sensed the change, and what had been weak, spindly little saplings felt their sap assume new speed, acquire more abundant nourishment; the offspring of the tree itself, and those of neighboring giants, began in turn their battle for life, the only chance they would ever have. There was no mercy, no brotherly aid; it was each for himself, a contest, not of weeks or months, but of decades and perhaps cen-turies, before some one plant, stronger by heredity, or exact situa-tion, or whatever we in our ignorance call luck, before some single tree would win through, reaching up and out, killing all competi-

tors. And unless it, in turn, was felled and burned to provide us with sliced bananas for breakfast, our nth great-grandchildren could stand at its base, look up and up, and, I hope, wonder and marvel as we were doing today.

I had, professorwise, poured out this account for Eric's benefit, and then we crept through the tangle of great roots, like maggots through cheese, though less skillfully, and to our delight found, here and there, the beginnings of spiny vines sprouting through the blossoms, and several of what appeared to be seedling trees.

When we returned to the trail, even after our exertions, we were not unpleasantly overheated, and this made patent another jungle character. In the sun outside, the thermometer had probably risen to 125° or thereabouts, while among the trees it was 78°. On the water of Golfito the glare was intense, but here we were surrounded by a cool, diffused twilight, and the universal greenness was sheer eye balm. In some of the semidesert bays to the north, sand flies and ticks made life almost unbearable, while here, as in so many other tropical jungles, we were troubled by no biting insects or other creatures, except for the usual quota of *bêtes rouges* if we insisted on sitting for long on inviting mossy logs, or lying at length on the soft jungle floor.

One thing is certain, no one can walk for long through a jungle and remain conceited. The Lord of Creation no longer strides over hills and plains, or up mountains. Exactly as an ant creeps over the ground in a field of grain three feet in height, so we must trudge slowly and silently in the dim cool shadows of these great growths, listening to strange sounds, sniffing odors from unknown sources. I know of no better cure for human vanity.

My physician-pupil, as we explored the Golfito jungle day after day, fairly boiled with excitement and wonder. He was not "Eric, or Little by Little," but "Eric, or Leaps and Bounds!" in his avid

curiosity. It was interesting to see him forming wrong conclusions about the animal life, logical conclusions based on superficial observations, and reasonable theories founded on apparent truths; all exactly the same as I had developed and believed in at one time. I watched the old magician of Nature forcing cards on Eric, who accepted them without question and believed implicitly in the results.

In the course of our walks, great bees, appearing enormous in the dim light, roared past like bombers going all out; carpenter bees, giving an anticlimactic slant to our simile, for they were laden with nonexplosive pollen. Two-inch wasps with emerald bodies and wings like living claret flew slowly, searching with diabolical thoroughness for equally gigantic tarantula spiders. A beetle, harlequined in mustard yellow and gray, crept up a palm with forelegs half a foot long. All this and more Eric saw, and from his lips burst a law: "Jungle life is gigantic." This I shattered by telling him of the thousands upon thousands of minute bees and wasps and beetles hidden everywhere about us. The giants were, by their size, forced upon his notice, but he might spend another two weeks and not come across another titan of its kind.

I saw his eyes fixed upon a leafy bush, and presently he walked over and looked down at a katydid on a leaf, sprawled out, motionless, a superkatydid with wings, each of which had an expanse of at least four square inches. Eric knew katydids, so with a quick grasp he picked up this one, and with equal celerity dropped it, his hands dripping blood. Two strong jaws had sunk deep into his thumb, and double lines of serried leg spines raked his fingers. If the song of this insect is up to its armament of pointed forceps and toothed rasps, it must sound like a buzz saw.

"In spite of all you've told me," said Eric, nursing his wounds, "I still hold to the gigantic idea.

"At least," he added, "I can safely say that most tropical creatures are brilliantly colored."

"You can say it, but unfortunately it is far from true," I answered, becoming stuffily pedantic. "If we credit Costa Rica with eight hundred species of birds, the number of dull-colored forms is greatly in excess over those with bright feathers. There are seventy gorgeously colored parrots and hummingbirds, but there are also seventy ant birds and wood hewers alone, to mention only two Quaker-hued jungle families, and so on. Toucans and trogons flash across the glades in front of you, but tinamous, doves, and wrens are almost unnoticed."

Eric clung fast to two other aphorisms, which I made no effort to debunk. These were, that tropical jungles are filled with creatures which are not what they seem, and others which appear to be what they are not. This Alice in Wonderland tangle he hugged to himself and enjoyed it as much as I always have and always shall.

"A woodpecker at last," said Eric, as a slender chocolate-colored bird hitched up a tree trunk. This was a case where the value of a bird is doubled in the hand, so I shot it. In structure of beak and stiffened, proplike tail feathers it was woodpecker, but with its three toes in front and one behind, it hopped several rungs up the avian ladder of evolution and took its place with the superior *Passeriformes*, together with swallows and nightingales. The only thing wrong with the bird was its human handle — wood hewer. The members of this group are peckers and tappers and knockers on wood, but in no sense hewers; that name should be applied to what we call woodpeckers, with their strong, hammerlike bills, built for hewing and banging on tree trunks, and even tunneling into them.

As we entered a small clearing, a sudden hissing and a loud swishing of wings marked the hasty flight of three black vultures which flapped heavily up through the branches. We found they had been feeding on a dead capuchin monkey, like those we had seen and chatted with a quarter of a mile back — jet-black little chaps with amber-colored face and chest. As I was leaving the clearing, I saw a stray bit of monkey flesh caught on a palm frond, apparently disgorged by the vultures in their haste. A movement on it drew my attention, and I saw walking over it a bluebottle fly of sorts, and as she walked, she sowed (there is no other word) a line of living maggots over the meat — so keen is competition here, with such speed is every opportunity seized.

Eric called me back and pointed to a high limb. There in full view, but until now invisible to us, was a king vulture, *el rey de los zopilotes* as the natives call him, hunched up, watching us. The glasses showed his clean ivory plumage, the brilliancy of the yellow and red wattles on head and neck, and the unwinking dead-white eyes, those amazing organs which can become telescopic or myopic at will.

"Even the vultures are colored like hummingbirds," said Eric, reverting to our earlier argument.

"Yes, but he was feeding with three black ones, so the dull plumages still have it, three hundred per cent."

Not long afterward George Swanson, our artist, called us to see a cluster of seven butterfly chrysalids hanging from the underside of a leaf. They were cellophane clear, and the yellow and black wings of embryo heliconian butterflies could be seen through them. But we had to look quickly, for they were hatching while we waited. One was already out but still clinging to the frayed-out ghost of its home, its wings soft, swollen, diminutive blobs of pigment. While we watched, breathless, a butterfly of the same species fluttered up, and with no hesitation flew directly to the still-swathed newly emerged one, and instantly mated with it. Here was a female two minutes out of her chrysalid, while her mate had wings tattered and torn, dull of luster, evidently near the end of his short jungle existence. In the glade we had seen death made the most of, exploited by vultures and flies; here, birth, or shall we say resurrection, played its instantaneous part in preparation for future generations.

As we reached the edge of the jungle, a monstrous insect, a huge scarlet and black grasshopper, rose with a whirr of wings and landed with a plop! on the front of my shirt. He took off before I could seize him, fluttered down the beach, and fell into the water close to shore. This strange performance on the part of such a strange-winged flier demanded investigation, and I scooped him up in a net and put him swiftly to sleep in the killing jar. Later examination showed no defect in his body armor: antennae and legs all accounted for, wings — spreading full nine inches — in perfect condition. When his body was dissected, however, not only was his aerial disability explained, but the wonder aroused that he could move at all, or was alive. In place of whatever organs function in a grasshopper's torso, there were fourteen large pupa cases of some kind of bluebottle fly, all ready to hatch, with round black eyes plainly visible, waiting to record impressions as soon as they could emerge from their present home in the fuselage of this living biplane. And I, a detached onlooker, knew not what to call evil, what good. Meditation on this single happening, involving fifteen living creatures, from the points of view of flies or grasshopper or myself, left the mind in a whirl of conflicting emotions. And the problem was rendered no simpler by the frustration of all possibility of success — the accidental interruption by myself of an excellent meal for some hungry fish.

On my last day in Golfito I went alone far into the jungle and settled down for observation at the edge of a marsh, where the stream sank into the soggy, mossy ground. While I was getting comfortable, a circle of little red-clawed crabs nervously *heiled* to me with their pincers held aloft, as they sidled and backed away from my vicinity.

For ten minutes I was completely baffled by a penetrating call note, perfect in its ventriloquial character. After I had made many attempts at translation into human speech, one word only satisfied me, *dough!* It came from every direction (*dough!*) including straight overhead (*dough!*) or whatever direction I happened to be looking (*dough!*). I finally decided that its slight, bell-like quality was that of some small frog. Then another note came to my ears, quite as ethereal and indefinite as to direction. This was a very sweet trill, with a delicate, tender cadence. It had much of the character of a phrase of the evening song of a wood thrush or veery. Several manakins came and went, twice drinking at the small stream, and suddenly I got my binoculars on a splendid chestnut-sided warbler in full spring plumage. I watched it fly-catching for many minutes, and wondered if, six weeks from now, I might not see this selfsame bird near New York City.

I swept the surrounding jungle with my glasses and noticed, from time to time, a blur at one spot. Careful focusing at last showed me that I was looking at the courtship dance of a long-tailed manakin. These are delightful little chunky birds, almost all black except for azure-blue back, crimson crest, and bright-orange legs and feet.

I crawled a few yards nearer, until I had a clear view. There were three males and a single leaf-green female. She sat very quietly and watched the proceedings without much apparent interest, while two of the male birds almost tore themselves apart for her. One at a time, they flew to a short, bare, horizontal twig, about two feet in length, and instantly began a jumping-jack performance.

From one end of the twig the bird bounced into the air in an oblique arc which landed it at the farther end, whence it instantly took off again. Its wings vibrated in a fluttering blur, and it uttered a drawn-out *chuuuuuuuuuuuwe! chuuuuuuuuuuuwe! chuuuuuuuu-uuuwe!* This sound strongly recalled the whiplike note of a towhee. Each utterance was perfectly synchronized with one performance — bounce, aerial arc, and drop; bounce, aerial arc, and drop. There was not the slightest hesitation between the landing and the take-off — it really gave the appearance of a bouncing rubber ball — and the completed turn consumed just one second of time. The first bird bounced twelve times in exactly as many seconds. The second bird then took the place of the first, bounced eighteen times, and vanished. Instantly the first bird resumed his perform-ance, and after eight bounces flew up close to the female. They sat quietly about an inch apart, and at once began a duet, revealing the source of the ventriloquial bell note which I had accredited to an amphibian.

The duet was absurdly simple, but melodious, the silly word *dough!* being invested by the birds with an infinite sweetness and liquid quality. Again and again the sequence was the same, twenty or thirty times, and always as follows: the female would say *dough!* and the male instantly responded with *dough-e!* or *dough-e-dough!* After the first two, the syllables merged, the female coming in on every first *dough* but never uttering the two- or three-syllabled phrase. These were purely the masculine part.

Finally, to my surprise, the thrushlike call came from near at hand, several times, and I found that the third male, who had not danced but only sat quietly a short distance away and overhead, was singing this third utterance, over and over, to himself. After several more minutes my cramped muscles demanded a slight shift, and with the movement, every manakin vanished.

This courtship has been described in part several times, but with a lack of exact detail. The *dough-e-dough* phrase has provided the native name in several Central American countries, written *Toledo*. The point of especial interest to me was the use of the same courting twig by two males in succession. Usually birds which have such elaborate courtships maintain a strictly individual domain or territory.

This manakin episode was a satisfying finale to our week in the Golfito jungle. As the *Zaca* slowly made her way out into the larger gulf, I looked back and saw as yet no visible man-made changes. It was exactly as the present Indians and their ancestors had always known it. And it was also the unaltered home of those other natives whose lives are lost in antiquity. Our only knowledge of them is of the dust of the men and the women lying in the innumerable graves scattered throughout the jungle, each individual provided with adequate and beautifully decorated pottery, and each with a charm of pure soft gold, some quaintly fashioned *huaco* of a bird or a frog or a little staring idol.

III
Jungle Life

CHAPTER 17

Hoatzins at Home

THE flight of the hoatzin resembles that of an overfed hen. The hoatzin's voice is no more melodious than the cry of a peacock, and less sonorous than an alligator's roar. The bird's grace is batrachian rather than avian, while the odor of its body resembles that of no bird untouched by dissolution. Still, zoologically considered, the hoatzin is probably the most remarkable and interesting bird living on the earth today.

It has successfully defied time and space. For it, the dial of the ages has moved more slowly than for the rest of organic life, and although living and breathing with us today, yet its world is an affair of two dimensions — a line of thorny saplings threaded along the muddy banks of a few tropical streams.

A bird in a cage cannot escape, and may be found month after month wherever the cage is placed. A stuffed bird in a case may resist disintegration for a century. But when we go to look for the bluebirds which nest in the orchard, they may have flown a half mile away in their search for food. The plover which scurries before us today on the beach may tonight be far away on the first lap of his seven-thousand-mile flight to the southward.

The hoatzin's status lies rather with the caged bird. In November in New York City an Englishman from British Guiana said to me, "Go to the Berbice River in British Guiana, and at the north end of the town of New Amsterdam, in front of Mr. Beckett's house, you will find hoatzins." Six months later, as I drove along a tropical river road, I saw three hoatzins perched on a low thorn bush at the river's edge in front of a house. And the river was the Berbice, and the house that of Mr. Beckett.

Thus are the hoatzins independent of space, as all other flying birds know it, and in their classic reptilian affinities — voice, actions, arms, fingers, habits — they bring close the dim epochs of past time, and renew for our inspection the youth of bird life on the earth. It is discouraging ever to attempt to translate habits fraught with so profound a significance into words, or to make them realistic, even with the aid of photographs.

We took a boat opposite Mr. Beckett's house and paddled slowly with the nearly flood tide up the Berbice River. It was two o'clock, the hottest time of the day. For three miles we drifted past the chosen haunts of the hoatzins. All were perched in the shade, quiet in the intense heat, squatting prostrate or sleepily preening their plumage. Now and then we saw a bird on her nest, always over the water. If she was sitting on eggs, she sat close. If young birds were in the nests, she half crouched or perched on the rim so that her body cast a shadow over the young.

The vegetation was not varied. Muckamucka was here and there in the foreground, with an almost solid line of bunduri pimpler, or thorn tree. This was the real home of the birds, and this plant forms the background whenever the hoatzin comes to mind. It is a growth which loves the water, and crowds down so that the rising of the tide, whether fresh or brackish, covers the mud in which it stands, so that it appears to be quite as aquatic as the mangrove which, here and there, creeps out alongside it.

The pimpler bears thorns of the first magnitude, often double, recurved, and at such diabolically unexpected places that, like barbed wire, it is impossible to grasp anywhere without drawing blood. Such a chevaux-de-frise would defend a trench against the most courageous regiment. The stems are light gray, greening toward the younger shoots, and the foliage is pleasantly divided into double lines of locustlike leaflets.

The plants were in full flower — dainty upright panicles of wisterialike pea blooms, pale violet and white with tiny buds of magenta. A faint, subdued perfume drifted from them through the tangle of branches. The fruit was ripening on many plants, in clusters of green, semicircular, flat, kidney pods. The low branches stretched gracefully waterwards in long sweeping curves. On these at a fork or at the crossing of two distinct branches, the hoatzins placed their nests, and with the soft-tissued leaflets they packed their capacious crops and fed their young.

Besides these two plants, which alone may be considered as forming the principal environment, two blooms were conspicuous at this season: a deep-calyxed round blossom of rich yellow — an hibiscus, which the Indians called *makoe,* and from the bark of which they made most excellent rope — and a vine which commonly crept up over the pimpler trees, regardless of water and thorns, and hung out twin blossoms in profusion, pink and pinkish white, trumpet-shaped, with flaring lips.

The midday life about this haunt of hoatzins was full of interest. Tody flycatchers of two species, yellow-breasted and streaked, were the commonest birds, and their little homes, like bits of tide-hung drift, swayed from the tips of the pimpler branches. They dashed to and fro regardless of the heat, and whenever we stopped, they came within a foot or two, curiously watching our every motion. Kiskadees hopped along the water's edge in the shade, snatching insects and occasionally splashing into the water after small fish. Awkward Guinea green herons, not long out of the nest, crept like shadow silhouettes of birds close to the dark water. High overhead, like flecks of jet against the blue sky, the vultures soared. Green dragonflies whirled here and there, and great blue-black bees fumbled in and out of the hibiscus, yellowed with pollen and too busy to stop a second in their daylong labor.

This little area held very strange creatures as well, some of which we saw even in our few hours' search. Four-eyed fish skittered over the water, pale as the ghosts of fish, and when quiet, showing only as a pair of bubbly eyes. Still more weird hairy caterpillars wriggled their way through the muddy, brackish current — aquatic larvae of a small moth which I had not seen since I found them in the trenches of Pará.

The only sound at this time of day was a drowsy but penetrating *tr-r-r-r-r-p!* made by a green-bodied, green-legged grasshopper of good size, whose joy in life seemed to be to lie lengthwise upon a pimpler branch and skreek violently at frequent intervals, giving his wings a frantic flutter at each utterance, and slowly encircling the stem.

In such environment the hoatzin lives and thrives, and, thanks to its strong body odor, has existed from time immemorial in the face of terrific handicaps. The odor is a strong musky one, not particularly disagreeable. I searched my memory at every whiff for something of which it vividly reminded me, and at last the recollection came to me — the smell, delectable and fearfully exciting in former years, of elephants at a circus, and not altogether elephants either, but a compound of one sixth sawdust, another part peanuts, another of strange animals, and three sixths swaying elephant. That, to my mind, exactly describes the odor of hoatzins as I sensed it among these alien surroundings.

As I have mentioned, the nest of the hoatzin was invariably built over the water, and we shall later discover the reason for this. The nests were sometimes only four feet above high water or, equally rarely, at a height of forty to fifty feet. From six to fifteen feet included the zone of four fifths of the nests of these birds. They varied much in solidity, some being frail and loosely put together, the dry, dead sticks which composed them dropping apart almost at a touch. Usually they were as well knitted as a heron's, and in about half the cases consisted of a recent nest built upon the foundations of an old one. There was hardly any cavity at the top, and the coarse network of sticks looked like a precarious resting place for eggs and an exceedingly uncomfortable one for young birds.

When we approached a nest, the occupant paid no attention until we actually came close to a branch, or shook it. She then rose, protesting hoarsely and lifting wings and tail as she croaked. At the last moment, often when only a yard away, she flew off and away to a distance of fifty feet or more. Watching closely, when she realized that we really had intentions on her nest, she returned and perched fifteen or twenty feet away, croaking continually, her mate a little farther off, and all the hoatzins within sight or hearing joining in sympathetic disharmony, all with synchronous lifting of tail and wings at each utterance.

The voice of the female is appreciably deeper than that of the male, having more of a gurgling character, like one of the notes of a curassow. The usual note of both sexes is an unwritable hoarse creaking sound, quite cicada or froglike.

Their tameness was astounding, and they would often sit unmoved while we were walking noisily about or focusing the camera within two yards. If several were sitting on a branch and one was shot, the others would often show no symptoms of concern or alarm, either at the noise of the gun or the fall of their companion. A hoatzin which may have been crouched close to the slain bird would continue to preen its plumage without a glance downward. When the young had attained their first full plumage, it was almost impossible to distinguish them from the older members of the flock except by their generally smaller size.

But the heart of our interest in the hoatzins centered in the nestlings. Some kind Providence directed the time of our visit, which I chose against the advice of some of the very inhabitants of New Amsterdam. It turned out that we were on the scene exactly at the right time. A week either way would have yielded much poorer results. The nestlings, in seven occupied nests, observed as we drifted along shore, or landed and climbed among the thorns, were in an almost identical stage of development. In fact, the greatest difference in size occurred between two nestlings of the same brood. Their down was a thin, scanty, fuzzy covering, and the flight feathers were less than a half inch in length. No age would have showed to better advantage every movement of wings or head.

When a mother hoatzin took reluctant flight from her nest, the young bird at once stood upright and looked curiously in every direction. No slacker he, crouching flat or awaiting his mother's directing cries. From the moment he was left alone he began to depend upon the warnings and signs which his great beady eyes and skinny ears conveyed to him. Hawks and vultures had swept low over his nest and mother unheeded. Coolies in their boats had paddled underneath with no more than a glance upward. Throughout his week of life, as through his parents' and their parents' parents' lives, no danger has disturbed his peaceful existence. Except for a sudden windstorm, such as that which the week before had upset nests and blown out eggs, it might be said that for the little hoatzin chicks, life held nothing but siestas and munchings of pimpler leaves.

But one little hoatzin, if he had any thoughts such as these, failed to count on the invariable exceptions to every rule, for this day the totally unexpected happened. Fate, in the shape of enthusiastic scientists, descended upon him. He was not for a second nonplussed. If we had concentrated upon him a thousand strong, by boats and by land, he would have fought the good fight for freedom and life as calmly as he waged it against us. And we found him no mean antagonist, and far from reptilian in his ability to meet new and unforeseen conditions.

His mother, who a moment before had been packing his capacious little crop with predigested pimpler leaves, had now flown off to an adjoining group of mangroves, where she and his father croaked to him hoarse encouragement. His flight feathers hardly reached beyond his finger tips, and his body was covered with a sparse coating of sooty-black down. So there could be no resort to flight. He must defend himself, bound to earth like his assailants.

Hardly had his mother left when his comical head, with thick, blunt beak and large intelligent eyes, appeared over the rim of the nest. His alert expression was increased by the suspicion of a crest on his crown where the down was slightly longer. Higher and higher rose his head, supported on a neck of extraordinary length and thinness. No more than this was needed to mark his absurd resemblance to some strange extinct reptile. A young dinosaur must have looked much like this, while for all that my glance revealed, I might have been looking at a diminutive Galápagos tortoise. Indeed, this simile came to mind often when I became more intimate with nestling hoatzins.

Sam, my black tree-climber, kicked off his shoes and began creeping along the horizontal limbs of the pimplers. At every step he

felt carefully with a calloused sole in order to avoid the longer of
the cruel thorns, and punctuated every yard with some gasp of pain
or muttered personal prayer: "Pleas' doan' stick me, Thorns!"

At last his hand touched the branch and it shook slightly. The
young bird stretched his mittened hands high above his head and
waved them a moment. With similar intent a boxer or wrestler
flexes his muscles and bends his body. One or two uncertain forward steps brought the bird to the edge of the nest at the base of
a small branch. There he stood, and raising one wing leaned heavily
against the stem, bracing himself. My man climbed higher, and the
nest swayed violently.

Now the brave little hoatzin reached up to some tiny side twigs,
and aided by the projecting ends of dead sticks from the nest, he
climbed with facility, his thumbs and forefingers apparently being
of more aid than his feet. It was fascinating to see him ascend,
stopping now and then to crane his head and neck far out, turtle-
wise. He met every difficulty with some new contortion of body or
limbs, often with so quick or so subtle a shifting as to escape my
scrutiny. The branch ended in a tiny crotch, and here, perforce,
ended his attempt at escape by climbing. He stood on the swaying
twig, one wing clutched tight, and braced himself with both feet.

Nearer and nearer crept Sam. Not a quiver on the part of the
little hoatzin. We did not know it, but inside that ridiculous head
there was definite decision as to a deadline. He watched the approach of this great strange creature — this Danger, this thing so
wholly new and foreign to his experience, and doubtless to all the
generations of his forebears. A black hand grasped the thorny
branch six feet from his perch, and like a flash he played his next
trick — the only remaining one he knew, one that set him apart
from all modern land birds, as the frog is set apart from the swallow.

The young hoatzin stood erect for an instant, and then both wings of the little bird were stretched straight back, not folded, birdwise, but dangling loosely and reaching well beyond the body. For a considerable fraction of time he leaned forward. Then without effort, without apparent leap or jump, he dived straight downward, as beautifully as a seal, direct as a plummet, and very swiftly. There was a scarcely noticeable splash, and as I gazed with real awe, I watched the widening ripples which undulated over the muddy water — the only trace of the whereabouts of the young bird.

It seemed as if no one, whether ornithologist, evolutionist, poet or philosopher could fail to be profoundly impressed at the sight we had seen. Here I was in a very real, a very modern boat, with the honk of motor horns sounding from the river road a few yards away through the bushes, in the shade of this tropical vegetation in the year nineteen hundred and sixteen; and yet the curtain of the past had been lifted, and I had been permitted a glimpse of what must have been common in the millions of years ago. It was a tremendous thing, a wonderful thing to have seen, and it seemed to dwarf all the strange sights which had come to me in all other parts of the earth's wilderness. I had read of these habits and had expected them, but like one's first sight of a volcano in eruption, no reading or description prepares one for the actual phenomenon.

I sat silently watching for the reappearance of the young bird. We tallied five pairs of eyes and yet many minutes passed before I saw the same little head and emaciated neck sticking out of the water alongside a bit of drift rubbish. The only visible thing was the protruding spikes of the bedraggled tail feathers. I worked the boat in toward the bird, halfheartedly, for I had made up my mind that this particular brave little bit of atavism deserved his freedom, so splendidly had he fought for it among the pimplers. Soon he ducked forward, dived out of sight, and came up twenty feet away among an inextricable tangle of vines. I sent a little cheer of well-wishing after him and we salvaged Sam.

Then we shoved out the boat and watched from a distance. Five or six minutes passed and a skinny, crooked, two-fingered mitten of an arm reared upward out of the muddy flood and the nestling, black and glistening, hauled itself out of water.

Thus must the first amphibian have climbed into the thin air. But the young hoatzin neither gasped nor shivered, and seemed as self-possessed as if this was a common occurrence in its life. There was not the slightest doubt, however, that this was its first introduction to water. Yet it had dived from a height of fifteen feet, about fifty times its own length, as cleanly as a seal leaps from a berg. It was as if a human child should dive *two hundred feet!*

In fifteen minutes more it had climbed high above the water and with unerring accuracy directly toward its natal bundle of sticks overhead. The mother now came close, and with hoarse rasping notes and frantic heaves of tail and wings lent encouragement. Just before we paddled from sight, when the little fellow had reached his last rung, he partly opened his beak and gave a little falsetto cry — a clear, high tone, tailing off into a guttural rasp. His splendid courage had broken at last; he had nearly reached the nest and he was aching to put aside all this terrible responsibility, this pitting of his tiny might against such fearful odds. He wanted to be a helpless nestling again, to crouch on the springy bed of twigs with a feather comforter over him and be stuffed at will with delectable pimpler pap. Such is the normal right destiny of a hoatzin chick, and the *whee-og!* wrung from him by the reaction of safety seemed to voice all these humanized statements.

CHAPTER 18

A Yard of Jungle

WITHIN five minutes the daily downpour of tropical rain would drench the jungle. At this moment the air was tense with electricity, absolutely motionless, and saturated with odorous moisture. The voices of all the wild creatures were hushed. The sense of mystery which is always so dominant in a tropical jungle seemed nearer, more vital, but more than ever a mystery. Its insistency made one oblivious of the great heat. The beating of one's heart became a perceptible sound, absurdly loud. All the swamp and jungle seemed listening to it.

Suddenly a voice came out of the heart of this mystery, and fittingly enough, the voice seemed something a little more or less than human, and also fittingly it uttered but a single word, and that word a question. And the listener realized that the answer to the question was the only thing which made life and work worthwhile. The throb of the blood in his veins was forgotten, and all his senses reached out to the sights and sounds and scents about him. And again the great black frog called from its slimy seat hidden in the still blacker water of the jungle swamp. Its voice was deep, guttural, and a little inhuman, but it asked as plainly as any honest man could ask, *Wh — y?* And after a minute, *Wh — y?*

I squatted in the center of a trail. Within walking distance behind me flowed the yellow waters of the Amazon, and the *igarapé*
from which the frogs had called was even now feeling the tidal
heave of the ocean. Ahead, the jungle stretched without a break
for three thousand miles or more. And here for a week I had suffered bodily torture, twisting into unhappy positions for hours at a
time, watching the birds which crowded the berry-laden foliage of
a single jungle tree. In the cool of early morning, throughout the
terrible breathless heat of midday and the drenching downpour
of afternoon, the frog and I put our questions. There was hope in
our interrogation. And my five senses all gave aid, and my hand
wrote down facts, and my mind pondered them.

In the very suburbs of Pará, at the mouth of the great Amazon
and within a hundred miles of the equator, I found a Mecca of
bird life. It was a gastronomic Mecca to be sure, a tall, slender, wild
cinnamon tree — *canela do mato* the natives called it. For a full
week I invited torture by attempting to study the bird life of this
single tree. This thing had not been done before; it might not be
worth the doing. But testing such possibilities are as important to
a naturalist's work as following along the more conventional and
consequently more certain lines of investigation. I had no time for
exploration of the surrounding country, so I had determined to
risk all my precious hours upon intensive observation in one spot.

The century before, a plantling had pushed up through the
jungle mold and had won success in the keen competition of the
tropics — the helpless, motionless, silent strife of the vegetable
folk. Year by year the lichen-sculptured trunk had pushed its way
upward toward light and air, miraculously saved from the deadly
embraces of the lianas which crawled forever through the jungle.
Today it had gained an accepted place. Although no forest giant,
with no great buttresses or masses of parasitic growths, it held up

its branches and twigs in full sunlight a hundred feet or more above the ground. And its twiggy fingers were laden with a wonderful harvest of fruit, uncounted berries which attracted the birds from distant roosts and drinking places.

Here, then, a thousand combinations of fate had led me, and here I suffered day by day. Bound to the earth like other normal men, I should have directed my eyes forward. Now I forced them upward for hours at a time, and all the muscles of neck and shoulders revolted. Then eyestrain and headache and a touch of fever followed, and I cast about for means to ameliorate my bodily ills. I dragged a canvas steamer chair to my place of vigil, and all my body was grateful.

In memory, there now remain only the high lights of new discoveries, the colorful moments of unalloyed realization of success. Nevertheless, this new method of tropical work brought its own new delights and trials. One joy lay in the very difficulties to be overcome. Every sense came into play. Sight, first and foremost, had been put to the most severe of tests in attempting to record the happenings against the glare of the sky high up among the foliage of this bit of jungle. I strained through my high-power glasses, until, when I looked without them, the world seemed withdrawn, dwarfed, as in the horrid imaginings of fever. The glasses gained in weight as I held them pointing vertically, until they fairly dropped from my aching arms. My ears strove to catch every song, every note which might prove a character of worth. The jungle scents played upon my emotions and sometimes dominated my work: the faint aroma from some invisible orchid overhead, the telltale musk from a passing mammal, the healthful scent of clean jungle mold. As for taste, I had tested the aromatic berries and fruit of my canella tree, and for science's sake had proved two warningly colored insects. My sense of feeling had operated involun-

tarily and wholly aside from my scientific desires. Whether stimulated by dozens of mosquitoes, scores of ants, or hundreds of
bêtes rouges, or "mucuims," the insistency of discomfort never
discouraged a primary desire to delve as deeply as possible into the
secrets of this small area of tropical jungle.

As I walked slowly about beneath the tree or lay back resting
on the chair, I seemed to be watching creatures of another world.
Whether I ogled them with glasses or now and then brought one
down with a charge of small shot, I was a thing of no account to
the berry-eating flocks high overhead. A vulture soaring lower than
usual passed over the tree, and the shadow of his partial eclipse of
the sun froze every bird to instant silence and complete immobility.
But my terrestrial activities wrought no excitement. The shot
whistled through the foliage, one of their number dropped from
sight, and life for the rest went on without a tremor. To ancestral
generations, danger had come always from above, not below.

The very difficulty of observation rendered this mode of research
full of excitement, and at the same time made my method of work
very simple. Against the sky, green, blue, or black feathers all appear black, and the first two days my glasses helped but little. For
several minutes I would watch some tiny bird which might have
been a yellow warbler had I been three thousand miles farther
north. After memorizing personal characters, scrutinizing its flight
and method of feeding, striving to fix its individuality, I would
secure the bird, and find in all probability that it was a calliste or
tanager of brilliant plumage. Tomorrow, if lucky, I might be able to
tell off the numbers of this species, to watch them and to know
that I was watching them. Recognition would not be by way
of the cerulean or topaz or amethystine hues of plumage, but by
the slight idiosyncrasies of flirting tail or wing or of general carriage.

Day by day, as I came to know better the jungle about me, I be-

gan to perceive a phase which did not change. Even when the sun shone most brightly, when the coolness of early morning had not yet passed, the mood of the Amazon jungle remained. It was con-sistent, this low swampy jungle, in its uniform, somber mystery. Of all places in the world this was probably fullest of life, both in numbers and diversity.

Beneath my tree I squatted silently. Just overhead the foliage might have been almost northern. The finely cut leaves were like willow, and at one side an oak, unusual but still an oak, reached out a thousand motionless leaves, breaking the glare into innumer-able patches. But ahead, the interlacing of vines and thorny ropes, the strange hold of serpentine lianas on every available trunk — all this could be only tropic.

The ground glistened here and there with a film of black water which revealed the swamp. Everywhere the mold and leaves of a hundred years lay scattered, the last fallen still green. Many feet above, great fans dangled, rayed fronds dry and crackling, fallen from high overhead, and suspended, waiting for the interfering twigs and foliage to die in turn and permit them to seek dissolu-tion in the mold.

The jungle was bright with flowers, but it was a sinister bright-ness — a flash of pigment, set off by the blackness of the shadows. Heliconia spikes gleamed like fixed scarlet lightning, zigzagging through the pungent air. Now and then a bunch of pleasing warm-hued berries reminded one of innocuous currants, but a second glance showed them ripening into swollen liver-hued globes which offered no temptation to taste. One tree dangled hideous purple cups filled with vermilion fruits, and not far away the color se-quence was reversed. A low-growing, pleasant-leaved plant lifted bursting masses of purple-black, all dripping like wounds upon the foliage below. Many flowers were unrecognizable save by their

fragrance and naked stamens, advertised neither by color nor form of blossom. I despaired of flowers worthy of the name, until close by my foot I saw a tiny plant with a comely, sweet-scented blossom, grateful to the eye and beautiful as our northern blooms are beautiful. The leaf was like scores lying about, and I realized that this was a sprouting of the giant tree. Nothing but the death of this monster could give the light and air which the little plant needed. It was doomed, but it had performed its destiny. It had limited that much of the beauty of the jungle lay far above the mold and stagnant water. And then I remembered the orchids high overhead. And the realization came that the low-growing blooms needed their glaring colors to outshine the dim, shadowy underjungle, and their nauseous fumes to outscent the musky vapors of decay.

The plants of the jungle won success either by elbowing their neighbors and fighting their path up to sunlight, or else by adapting their needs to the starvation meed of air and light allotted to the lowly growths. The big-leaved chiracas had found another means of existence. They lived like permanent rockets, bursting in mid-air. A long curved stem shot up and reached far out into space. It was so slender as to be almost invisible in the dim light. At its tip radiated a great burst of foliage, leaves springing out in all directions and absorbing nutrition which a sapling growing amid the undergrowth could not possibly do.

From daybreak to dark the canella tree was seldom deserted. Usually a score or more birds fluttered and fed among its branches, and true to tropic laws, there were comparatively few individuals but a multitude of species. In the few hours I was able to devote to its study, I identified seventy-six different kinds, and together with those which I saw but could not name, I judge that more than a hundred species must have come to the berries during that week in early May. The first day I secured sixteen specimens, all different;

and the following day yielded fourteen more, only one of which was a duplicate of the first day's results.

The bird visitors to the tree arrived in one of two characteristic ways. Many came direct and swiftly, singly or in pairs, flying straight and with decision. These came from a distance, with full knowledge of the berries. They fed quietly, and when satiated, flew off. The second method of arrival was wholly casual — loose flocks drifting slowly from the neighboring jungle, sifting into the tree, and feeding for a time before passing on. When these left, it was rather hastily, and in answer to the chirps and calls of the members of their flock who had not been beguiled by the berries and hence had forged steadily ahead.

These more or less well-defined flocks are very characteristic of all tropical jungles. Little assemblages of flycatchers, callistes, tanagers, ant birds, manakins, wood hewers, and woodpeckers are drawn together by some intangible but very social instinct. Day after day they unite in these fragile fraternities which drift along, gleaning from leaves, flowers, branches, trunks, or ground, each bird according to its structure and way of life. They are so held together by a gregarious instinct that time after time the same heterogeneous flock may be observed, identifiable by peculiarities of one or several of its members. The only recognizable bond is vocal — a constant low calling; half-unconscious, absent-minded little signals which keep the members in touch with one another, spurring on the laggards, retarding the overswift.

While I watched, there came to my tree a single species of pigeon, two hawks and two parrots, four hummingbirds, and an equal number of toucans and woodpeckers. The remaining fifty-nine were all passerine birds, of which there were eight each of the families of flycatchers, manakins, and cotingas. Eleven were tanagers.

The greedy, noisy parrakeets were always the center of commotion, wasting more berries than they ate. The toucans, those bizarre birds of whose lives we know so little, yelped and called and bathed in the water caught in the stubs of branches, and fed to repletion. All the flycatchers forgot their usual diet and took to berrying as ardently as the tanagers themselves. Not all the birds came to feed on the berries. A wren hunted insects among the branches, and a hawk found a giant snail crawling up the trunk and devoured it. The insect-eaters of the trunk numbered nine and showed no interest in the berries. Two were woodpeckers and seven wood hewers.

These latter are a strange tropical family four hundred strong, and all the very essence of protective coloring. Their habits of life make of them wandering bits of bark, easy to detect when they are in motion, but vanishing utterly when they are quiet. Their similarity in dress is remarkable. They may be large or small, short- or long-tailed, with beaks blunt, sharp, straight, curved, thick, or needle-pointed. In these characters they differ; by these points they must know one another. But their colors are almost identical. Their olives or browns invariably warm into rich foxy rufous on wings and tail, while over head and shoulders a shower of light streaks has fallen, bits of sunlight fixed in down.

Further details belong to the literature of ornithology. But the colors of the berry hunters — these baffle description, yet we cannot pass them by in silence. The blood and orange splashed on black of the toucans, the scarlet and yellow of woodpeckers, the soft greens and buffs of flycatchers, all these paled when a flock of manakins or tanagers or honey creepers came to the tree. Every precious stone found its counterpart in the metallic hues of these exquisite feathered folk.

The glory of all was the opal-crowned manakin, a midget in

green coat and sulphur waistcoat, with a cap of scaly, iridescent, silvery mother-of-pearl plates, in no way akin to feathers. Until now the life of this hop-o'-my-thumb, like those of all his ancestors, had gone smoothly on, with never a human to admire, to wonder, and vainly to echo the question of the great black frog, W*h — y*?

On the last day of my stay I walked slowly up the trail toward the *canela do mato*. For the last time I strained upward at the well-known branches, and with the very movement there came the voice of the swamp. Its tone was insistent, with a tinge of accusation, a note of censure. W*h — y*? and after a little time, W*h — y*?

I looked about me despairingly. What had I learned after all? Was there any clearing up of the mystery of the jungle? Had my week of scrutiny brought me any closer to the real intimacies of evolution? Or — evading these questions for the time — was there nothing I could do in the few precious moments left?

In five minutes I would turn my back on all this wildness, this jungle seething with profound truths and great solutions within arm's reach. I would pass to the ocean where monotony compels introspection, and finally to the great center of civilization where the veneer covers up all truths.

Even if my studies had taught only the lesson of the tremendous insurgence of life, could I not emphasize this, make it a more compelling factor to be considered in future efforts toward the frog's question and mine?

My eyes left the foliage overhead and sought the ground. Acting on impulse, I brought from my camping stores an empty war bag and scraped together an armful of leaves, sticks, moss, earth, mold of all sorts. Four square feet of jungle debris went into my bag, and I shouldered it.

Then I said adieu to my trail and my tree — a sorrowful leave-taking, as is always my misfortune. For the bonds which bind me to a place or a person are not easily broken. And, as usual, when the trail passed from view, the ideal alone remained. The thoughts of mosquitoes, of drenching, of hours of breathless, disappointed waiting, all sank in the memory of the daily discoveries, the mental delights of new research.

A week later, when the sky line was unbroken by land, when a long ground swell waved but did not disturb the deep blue of the open sea, I unlaced my bag of jungle mold. Armed with forceps, lens, and vials, I began my search. For days I had gazed upward; now my scrutiny was directed downward. With binoculars I had scanned without ceasing the myriad leaves of a great tree; now with lens or naked eye I sought for life or motion on single fallen leaves and dead twigs. When I studied the life of the great tree, I was in the land of Brobdingnag; now I was verily a Gulliver in Lilliput. The cosmos in my war bag teemed with interest as deep and as inviting as any in the jungle itself.

When I began work, I knew little of what I should find. My vague thoughts visualized ants and worms, and especially I anticipated unearthing myriads of the unpleasant "mucuims," or *bêtes rouges*, whose hosts had done all in their power to make life in the jungle unhappy.

Day by day my vials increased. Scores of creatures evaded my search; many others, of whose kind I had captured a generous number, I allowed to escape.

My Lilliputian census was far from the mere aggregation of ants and worms which I had anticipated, and a review of the whole showed that hardly any great group of living creatures was unrepresented.

As hinting of the presence of wild animals, a bunch of rufous hairs had in some way been tweaked from a passing agouti. Man himself was represented in the shape of two wads which had dropped from my gunshots sometime during the week. One had already begun to disintegrate and sheltered half a dozen diminutive creatures. Five feathers were the indications of birds, two of which were brilliant green plumes from a calliste. Of reptiles there was a broken skull of some lizard, long since dead, and the eggshell of a lizardling which had hatched and gone forth upon his mission into the jungle. A third reptilian trace may have been his nemesis — a bit of shed snakeskin. The group of amphibians was present even in this square of four feet — a very tiny, dried, black, and wholly unrecognizable little frog. Fishes were absent, though from my knees as I scraped up the debris, I could almost have seen a little *igarapé* in which dwelt scores of minnows.

As I delved deeper and examined the mold more carefully for the diminutive inhabitants, I found that this thin film from the floor of the jungle appeared to have several layers, each with its particular fauna. The upper layer was composed of recently fallen leaves, nuts, seeds, and twigs, dry and quite fresh. Here were colonies of small ants and huge, solitary ones; here lived in hiding small moths and beetles and bugs, awaiting dusk to fly forth through the jungle. The middle layer was by far the most important, and in it lived four fifths of all the small folk. The lowest layer was one of matted roots and clayey soil, and its animal life was meager.

Between the upper and the middle strata were sprouting nuts and seeds, with their blanched roots threaded downward into the rich dark mold, and the greening cotyledons curling upward toward light and warmth. Thus had the great bird-filled canella begun its life. In my war bag were a score of potential forest giants doomed to death in the salt ocean. But for my efforts toward the W$h - y$, their fate might have been very different.

Some of the half-decayed leaves were very beautiful. Vistas of pale, bleached fungus lace trailed over the rich mahogany-colored tissues, studded here and there with bits of glistening, transparent quartz. Here I had many hints of a world of life beyond the power of the unaided eye. And here too the grosser fauna scrambled, hopped, or wriggled. Everywhere were tiny chrysalids and cocoons, many empty. Now and then a plaque of eggs, almost microscopic, showed veriest pinpricks where still more minute parasites had made their escape. When one contracted the field of vision to this world where leaves were fields and fungi loomed as forests, competition, tragedy lessened not at all. Minute seeds mimicked small beetles in shape and in tracery of patterns. Bits of bark simulated insects, a patch of fungus seemed a worm, while the mites themselves were invisible until they moved. Here and there I discovered a lifeless boulder of emerald or turquoise — the metallic cuirass of some long-dead beetle.

Some of the scenes which appeared as I picked over the mold, suddenly unfolding after an upheaval of debris, were like Aladdin's cave. Close to the eye appeared great logs and branches protruding in confusion from a heaped-up bank of diamonds. Brown, yellow, orange, and white colors played over the scene; and now over a steep hill came a horrid, ungainly creature with enormous proboscis, eight legs, and a shining, liver-colored body spotted with a sickly hue of yellow. It was studded with short, stiff, horny hairs — a mite by name, but under the lens a terrible monster. I put some of these on my arm, to see if they were the notorious "mucuims" which tortured us daily. Under the lens I saw the hideous creature stop in its awkward progress, and as it prepared to sink its proboscis, I involuntarily flinched, so fearful a thing seemed about to happen.

The lesser organisms defy description. They are nameless except in the lists of specialists, and probably most are of new unnamed forms. The only social insects were small twigfuls of ant and termite colonies, with from five to fifteen members. All others were isolated, scattered. Life here, so far beneath the sunlight, is an individual thing. Flocks and herds are unknown; the mob has no place here. Each tiny organism must live its life and meet its fate singlehanded.

Little pseudo scorpions were very abundant, and I could have vialed hundreds. They rushed out excitedly and, unlike all the other little beings, did not seek to hide. Instead, when they were disturbed, they sought open spaces, walking slowly and brandishing and feeling ahead with their great pincer-tipped arms, as long as their entire body. When irritated or frightened, they scurried backwards, holding up their chelae in readiness.

Mites were the most abundant creatures, equaling the ants in number, always crawling slowly along, tumbling over every obstacle in their path and feeling their way awkwardly. Their kinds were numerous, all villainous in appearance. Ticks were less common but equally repellent. Small spiders and beetles were occasionally found, and hundred-legged wrigglers fled to shelter at every turn of a leaf. The smallest snails in the world crawled slowly about, some flat-shelled, others turreted. Tiny earthworms, bright red and very active, crept slowly through fungus jungles until disturbed, when they became an amazingly active tangle of twisting curves, dancing all about. Simple insects, which we shall have to call *Collembola*, were difficult to capture. They leaped with agility many times their own length, and when quiescent, looked like bits of fungus. As for the rest, only Adam and a few specialists hidden in museums could call them by name. They were a numerous company, some ornamented with weird horns and fringes and patterns, others long of legs or legless, swift of foot or curling up into minute balls of animate matter.

One thing was evident early in my exploration: I was in a world of little people. No large insects were in any of the debris. The largest would be very small in comparison with a May beetle. And another thing was the durability of chitin. The remains of beetles, considering the rareness of living ones, were remarkable. The hard wing cases, the thorax armor, the segments of wasps, eyeless head masks still remained perfect in shape and vivid in color. Even in the deepest layers where all else had disintegrated and returned to the elements, these shards of death were as new.

And the smell of the mold, keen and strong as it came to my nostrils an inch away — it was pungent, rich, woody. It hinted of the age-old dissolution, century after century, which had been going on. Leaves had fallen, not in a sudden autumnal downpour, but in a never-ending drift, day after day, month after month. With a daily rain for moisture, with a temperature of three figures for the quicker increase of bacteria, and an excess of humidity to foster quick decay, the jungle floor was indeed a laboratory of vital work — where only analytic chemistry was allowed full sway, and the mystery of synthetic life was ever handicapped.

Before the vessel docked, I had completed my task and had secured over five hundred creatures of this lesser world. At least twice as many remained, but when I made my calculations, I estimated that the mold had sheltered only a thousand organisms plainly visible to the eye.

And when I had corked my last vial and the steward had removed the last pile of shredded debris, I leaned back and thought of the thousand creatures in my scant four square feet of mold. There came to mind a square mile of jungle floor with its thin layer of fallen leaves sheltering more than six billion creatures. Then I recalled the three thousand straight miles of jungle which had lain west of me, and the hundreds of miles of wonderful unbroken forest north and south, and my mind became a blank. And then from the mist of unnamable numerals, from this uncharted

arithmetical census, there came to memory a voice, deep and guttural — and this time the slow enunciation was jeering, hopeless
of answer, *Wh — y?* and soon afterwards, *Wh — y?* And I packed
up my last box of vials and went on deck to watch the sunset.

CHAPTER 19

A Bit of Uselessness

A MOST admirable servant of mine risked his life to reach a magnificent Bornean orchid, and tried to poison me an hour later when he thought I was going to take the plant away from him. This does not mean necessarily that we should look with suspicion upon all gardeners and lovers of flowers. It emphasizes, rather, the fact of the universal and deep-rooted appreciation of the glories of the vegetable kingdom. Long before the fatal harvest time I am certain that Eve must have plucked a spray of apple blossoms with perfect impunity.

A vast amount of bad poetry and a much lesser quantity of excellent verse has been written about flowers, much of which follows to the letter Mark Twain's injunction about truth. It must be admitted that the relations existing between the honeysuckle and the bee are basely practical and wholly selfish. A butterfly's admiration of a flower is no whit less than the blossom's conscious appreciation of its own beauties! There are ants which spend most of their life making gardens, knowing the uses of fertilizers, mulching, planting seeds, exercising patience, recognizing the time of ripeness, and gathering the edible fruit. But this is underground, and the ants are blind.

There is a bird, however — the bowerbird of Australia — which appears to take real delight in bright things, especially pebbles and flowers, for their own sake. Its little lean-to, or bower of sticks, which has been built in our own Zoological Park in New York City, is fronted by a cleared space, which is usually mossy. To this it brings its colorful treasures, sometimes a score of bright star blossoms, which are renewed when faded and replaced by others. All this has, probably, something to do with courtship, which should inspire a sonnet.

From the first pre-Egyptian who crudely scatched a lotus on his dish of clay down to Drinkwater's jolly Feckenham men, the human race has given to flowers something more than idle curiosity, something less than mere earnest of fruit or berry.

At twelve thousand feet I have seen one of my Tibetans, with nothing but a few shreds of straw between his bare feet and the snow, probe around the south edge of melting drifts until he found brilliant little primroses to stick behind his ears. I have been ushered into the little-used, musty best parlor of a New England farmhouse and seen fresh vases of homely, old-fashioned flowers — so recently placed for my edification that drops of water still glistened like dewdrops on the dusty plush mat beneath. I have sat in the seat of honor of a Dyak communal house, looked up at the circle of all too recent heads, and seen a gay flower in each hollow eye socket, placed there for my approval. With a cluster of colored petals swaying in the breeze, one may at times bridge centuries or span the earth.

And now as I sit writing these words in my jungle laboratory, a small dusky hand steals around an aquarium and deposits a beautiful spray of orchids on my table. The little face appears, and I can distinguish the high cheekbones of Indian blood, the flattened nose and slight kink of Negro, and the faint trace of white — probably of some long-forgotten Dutch sailor who came and went to Guiana while New York City was still a browsing ground for moose.

So neither race nor age nor mélange of blood can eradicate the love of flowers. It would be a wonderful thing to know about the first garden that ever was, and I wish that Best Beloved had demanded this. I am sure it was long before the day of dog, or cow, or horse, or even she who walked alone. The only way we can imagine it is to go to some wild part of the earth where are fortunate people who have never heard of seed catalogues or lawn mowers.

Here in British Guiana I can run the whole gamut of gardens within a few miles of where I am writing. A mile above my laboratory upriver is the thatched *benab* of an Akawai Indian — whose house is a roof, whose rooms are hammocks, whose estate is the jungle. Degas can speak English, and knows the use of my 28-gauge double-barrel well enough to bring us a constant supply of delicious bush meat — peccary, deer, monkey, bush turkeys, and agoutis. Old Grandmother has no language but her native Akawai. She is a good friend of mine, and we hold long conversations, neither of us bothering with the letter, but only the spirit of communication. She is a tiny person, bowed and wrinkled as only an old Indian squaw can be, always jolly and chuckling to herself, although Degas tells me that the world is gradually darkening for her. And she vainly begs me to clear the film which is slowly closing over her eyes. She labors in a true landscape garden — the small circle wrested with cutlass and fire from the great jungle and kept free only by constant cutting of the vines and lianas which creep out almost in a night, like sinister octopus tentacles, to strangle the strange upstarts and re-jungle the bit of sunlit glade.

Although to the eye a mass of tangled vegetation, an Indian's garden may be resolved into several phases — all utterly practical, with color and flowers as mere by-products. First come the provisions, for if Degas were not hunting for me, and eating my rations, he would be out with bow and blowpipe, or fishhooks, while the women worked all day in the cassava field. It is his part to clear and burn the forest; it is hers to grub up the rich mold, to plant, and to weed. Plots and beds are unknown, for in every direction are fallen trees, too large to burn or be chopped up, and great sprawling roots. Between these, sprouts of cassava and banana are stuck, and the yams and melons which form the food of these primitive people. Cassava is as vital to these Indians as the air they breathe. It is their wheat and corn and rice, their soup and salad and dessert, their ice and their wine, for besides being their staple food, it provides *casareep*, which preserves their meat, and *piwarie*, which, like excellent wine, brightens life for them occasionally, or dims it if overindulged in — which is equally true of food, or companionship, or the oxygen in the air we breathe.

Besides this cultivation, Grandmother has a small group of plants which are only indirectly concerned with food. One is *kunami*, whose leaves are pounded into pulp and used for poisoning the water of jungle streams, with the surprising result that the fish all leap out on the bank and can be gathered as one picks up nuts. When I first visited Grandmother's garden, she had a few pitiful little cotton plants from whose stunted bolls she extracted every fiber and made a most excellent thread. In fact, when she made some bead aprons for me, she rejected my spool of cotton and chose her own, twisted between thumb and finger. I sent for seed of the big Sea Island cotton, and her face almost unwrinkled with delight when she saw the packets with seed larger than she had ever known.

Far off in one corner I make certain I have found beauty for beauty's sake, a group of exquisite caladiums and amaryllis, beautiful flowers and rich green leaves with spots and slashes of white and crimson. But this is the hunter's garden, and Grandmother has no part in it, perhaps is not even allowed to approach it. It is the *beena* garden — the charms for good luck in hunting. The similarity of the leaves to the head or other parts of deer or peccary or red-gilled fish decides the most favorable choice, and the acrid, smarting juice of the tuber rubbed into the skin, or the hooks and arrows anointed, is considered sufficient to produce the desired result. Long ago I discovered that this demand for immediate physical sensation was a necessary corollary of doctoring, so I always give two medicines — one for its curative properties, and the other, bitter, sour, acid, or anything disagreeable, for arousing and sustaining faith in my ability.

The Indian's medicine plants, like his true name, he keeps to himself, and although I feel certain that Grandmother had somewhere a toothache bush or pain leaves — yarbs and simples for various miseries — I could never discover them. Half a dozen tall tobacco plants, brought from the far interior, eked out the occasional tins of cigarettes in which Degas indulged, and always the flame-colored little buck peppers lightened up the shadows of the *benab*, as hot to the palate as their color to the eye.

One day, just as I was leaving, Grandmother led me to a palm nearby, and to one of its ancient frond sheaths was fastened a small brown branch to which a few blue-green leaves were attached. I had never seen anything like it. She mumbled and touched it with her shriveled, bent fingers. I could understand nothing, and sent for Degas, who came and explained grudgingly, "Me no know what for — *toko-nook* just name — have got smell when yellow." And so at last I found the bit of uselessness, which, carried onward and developed in ages to come, as it had been elsewhere in ages past, was to evolve into botany, and backyard gardens, and greenhouses, and wars of roses, and beautiful paintings, and music with a soul of its own, and verse more than human. To Degas the *toko-nook* was "just name," and it was nothing more. But he was forgiven, for he had all unwittingly sowed the seeds of religion, through faith in his glowing caladiums. But Grandmother, though all the sunlight seemed dusk, and the dawn but as night, yet clung to her little plant, her orchid, whose glory was that it was of no use whatsoever, but in months to come would be yellow, and would smell.

Farther downriver, in the small hamlets of the bovianders — the people of mixed blood — the practical was still necessity, but almost every thatched and wattled hut had its swinging orchid branch, and perhaps a hideous painted tub, with picketed rim, in which grew a golden splash of croton. This ostentatious floweritis might furnish a theme for a wholly new phase of the subject — for in almost every respect these people are less worthy human beings — physically, mentally, and morally — than the Indians. But one cannot shift literary overalls for philosophical paragraphs in mid-article, so let us take the little river steamer downstream for forty miles to the coast of British Guiana, and there see what Nature herself does in the way of gardens. We drive twenty miles or more before we reach Georgetown, and the sides of the road are lined for most of the distance with huts and hovels of East Indian coolies and native Guiana Negroes. Some are made of boxes, others of bark, more of thatch or rough-hewn boards and barrel staves, and some of split bamboo. But they resemble one another in several respects — all are ramshackle, all lean with the grace of Pisa, all have shutters and doors so that at night they may be hermetically closed, and all are half hidden in the folds of a curtain of flowers. The most shiftless, unlovely hovel, poised ready to return to its original chemical elements, is embowered in a mosaic of color which in a northern garden would be worth a king's ransom.

The deep trench which extends along the front of these sad

dwellings is sometimes blue with water hyacinths; next the water disappears beneath a maze of tall stalks topped with a pink mist of lotus; then come floating lilies and more hyacinths. Wherever there is sufficient clear water, the wonderful curve of a coconut palm is etched upon it, reflection meeting palm to form a dendritic pattern unequaled in human devising.

Over a hut of rusty oilcans bougainvillaea stretches its glowing branches, sometimes cerise, sometimes purple, or allamandas fill the air with a golden haze from their glowing searchlights, either hiding the huts altogether or softening their details into picturesque ruins. I remember one coolie dwelling which was dirtier and less habitable than the meanest stable, and all around it were hundreds upon hundreds of frangipani blooms — the white-and-gold temple flowers of the East — giving forth of scent and color all that a flower is capable of, to alleviate the miserable blot of human construction. Now and then a flamboyant tree comes into view, and as at night the headlights of an approaching car eclipse all else, so this tree of burning scarlet draws eye and mind from adjacent human-made squalor. In all the tropics of the world I scarcely remember to have seen more magnificent color than in these unattended, willful-grown gardens.

In tropical cities such as Georgetown, there are very beautiful private gardens, and the public one is second only to that of Java. But for the most part one is as conscious of the very dreadful borders of brick, or bottles, or conches, as of the flowers themselves. Someone who is a master gardener will some day write of the possibilities of a tropical garden, which will hold the reader as does desire to behold the gardens of Carcassonne itself.

CHAPTER 20

The Bay of Butterflies

BUTTERFLIES doing strange things in very beautiful ways were in my mind when I sat down, but by the time my pen was uncapped my thoughts had shifted to rocks. The ink was refractory and a vigorous flick sent a shower of green drops over the sand on which I was sitting, and as I watched the ink settle into the absorbent quartz — the inversions of our grandfathers' blotters — I thought of what jolly things the lost ink might have been made to say about butterflies and rocks, if it could have flowed out slowly in curves and angles and dots over paper — for the things we might have done are always so much more worthy than those which we actually accomplish. When at last I began to write, a song came to my ears and my mind again looped backward. At least, there came from the very deeps of the water beyond the mangroves a low, metallic murmur; and my Stormouth says that in Icelandic *sangra* means to murmur. So what is a murmur in Iceland may very well be a song in Guiana. At any rate, my pen would have to do only with words of singing catfish; yet from butterflies to rock to fish, all was logical looping — mental giant swings which came as relaxation after hours of observation of unrelated sheer facts.

The singing cats, so my pen consented to write, had serenaded me while I crossed the Cuyuni in a canoe. There arose deep, liquid, vibrating sounds, such as those I now heard, deep and penetrating as if from some submarine gong — a gong which could not be thought of as wet, for it had never been dry. As I stopped paddling, the sound became absolute vibration, the canoe itself seemed to tremble, the paddle tingled in my hands. It was wholly detached; it came from whatever direction the ear sought it. Then, without dying out, it was reinforced by another sound, rhythmical, abrupt, twanging, filling the water and air with a slow measure on four notes. The water swirled beside the canoe, and a face appeared — a monstrous, complacent face, such as Böcklin would love — a face inhuman in possessing the quality of supreme contentment. Framed in the brown waters, the head of the great, grinning catfish rose, and slowly sank, leaving outlines discernible in ripples and bubbles with almost Cheshire persistency. One of my Indians, passing in his dugout, smiled at my peering down after the fish, and murmured, "Boom-boom."

Then came a day when one of these huge, amiable, living smiles blundered into our net, a smile a foot wide and six feet long, and even as he lay quietly awaiting what fate brought to great catfish, he sang, both theme and accompaniment. His whole being throbbed with the continuous deep drumming as the thin, silky walls of his swim bladder vibrated in the depths of his body. The oxygen in the air was slowly killing him, and yet his swan song was possible because of an inner atmosphere so rich in this gas that it would be unbreathable by a creature of the land. Nerve and muscle, special expanse of circling bones, swim bladder and its tenuous gas — all these combined to produce the aquatic harmony. But as if to load this contented being with largesse of apparently useless abilities, the two wide-spreading fin spines — the fins which correspond to our arms — were swiveled in rough-ridged cups at what might have been shoulders, and when moved back and forth, the stridulation troubled all the water, and the air, too, with the muffled, twanging *rip, rip, rip, rip.* The two spines were tuned separately, the right being a full tone lower, and the backward drawing of the bow gave a higher note than its forward reach. So alternately, at a full-second tempo, the four tones rose and fell, carrying out some strange Silurian theme — a muffled cadence of undertones which emphasized the mystery of their author and cause, yet merged smoothly with the cosmic orchestra of wind and ripples and distant rain.

So the great, smooth, arching lift of granite rocks at our bungalow's shore, where the giant catfish sang, was ever afterward Boomboom Point. And now I sat close by on the sand and strove to think anew of my butterflies, for they were the reason of my being there that brilliant October afternoon. But still my pen refused, hovering about the thing of ultimate interest as one leaves the most desired book to the last. For again the ear claimed dominance, and I listened to a new little refrain over my shoulder. I pictured a tiny sawhorse, and a midget who labored with might and main to cut through a never-ending stint of twigs. I chose to keep my image to the last, and did not move or look around until there came the slightest of tugs at my knee, and into view clambered one of those beings who are so beautiful and bizarre that one almost thinks they should not be. My second singer was a beetle — an awkward, enormous, serious, brilliant harlequin beetle, with six-inch antennae and great wing covers which combined the hues of the royal robes of Queen Thi, tempered by thousands of years of silent darkness in the underground tombs at Sakkara, with the grace of curve and angle of equally ancient characters on the hill tombs of Fukien. On a background of olive ocher there blazed great splashes and characters of the red of jasper framed in black.

Toward the front Nature had tried heavy black stippling, but it clouded the pattern and she had given it up in order that I might think of Egypt and Cathay.

But the thing which took the beetle quite out of a world of reasonable things was his forelegs. They were outrageous, and he seemed to think so, too, for they got in his way, and caught in wrong things and pulled him to one side. They were three times the length of his other limbs, spreading sideways a full thirteen inches, long, slender, beautifully sculptured, and forever reaching out in front for whatever long-armed beetles most desire. And his song, as he climbed over me, was squeaky and sawlike, and as he walked, he doddered, head trembling as an old man shakes in final acquiescence in the futility of life.

But in this great-armed beetle it was a nodding of necessity, a doddering of desire, the drawing of the bow across the strings in a hymn of hope which had begun in past time with the first stridulation of ancient insects. Today the fiddling vibrations, the Song of the Beetle, reached out in all directions. To the majority of jungle ears it was only another note in the day's chorus: I saw it attract a flycatcher's attention, hold it a moment, and then lose it. To me it came as a vitally interesting tone of deep significance, for whatever emotions it might arouse in casual ears, its goal was another great-armed beetle, who might or might not come within its radius. With unquestioning search the fiddler clambered on and on, over me and over flowers and rocks, skirting the ripples and vanishing into a maelstrom of waving grass. Long after the last awkward lurch there came back *zizz*-ing squeaks of perfect faith, and I hoped, as I passed beyond the periphery of sound, that instinct and desire might direct their rolling sphere of vibrations toward the one whose ear, whether in antenna, or thorax, or femoral tympanum, had, through untold numbers of past lives, been attuned to its rhythm.

Two thousand miles north of where I sat, or ten million five hundred and sixty thousand feet (for, like Bunker Bean's book-keeper, I sometimes like to think of things that way), I would look out of the window one morning in days to come and thrill at the sight of falling flakes. The emotion would very probably be sentiment — the memory of wonderful northland snowstorms, of huge fires, of evenings with Roosevelt when discussions always led to unknowable fields, when book after book yielded its phrase or sentence of pure-gold thought. On one of the last of such evenings I found a forgotten joy-of-battle speech of Huxley's, which stimulated two full days and four books reread — while flakes swirled and invisible winds came swiftly around the eaves over the great trophies — we longing with our whole souls for an hour of talk with that splendid old fighting scientist.

These are thoughts which come at first snow, thoughts humanly narrow and personal compared to the later delights of snow itself — crystals and tracks, the strangeness of freezing and the mystery of melting. And they recurred now because for days past I had idly watched scattered flurries of lemon yellow and of orange butterflies drift past Kartabo. Down the two great Guiana rivers they came, steadily progressing yet never hurrying; with zigzag flickering flight they barely cleared the trees and shrubs, and then skimmed the surface, vanishing when ripples caught the light, redoubled by reflection when the water lay quiet and polished. For month after month they passed, sometimes absent for days or weeks but soon to be counted at earliest sunup, always arousing renewed curiosity, always bringing to mind the first flurry of winter.

We watch the autumn passing of birds with regret, but when the bluebirds warble their way southward, we are cheered with the hope and the knowledge that some, at least, will return. Here, vast stretches of country, perhaps all Guiana and how much of Brazil and Venezuela no one knows, poured forth a steady stream of yellow and orange butterflies. They were very beautiful and they danced and flickered in the sunlight, only this was no temporary shifting to a pleasanter clime or a land of more abundant flowers, but a migration in the grim old sense which Cicero loved: *Non dubitat . . . migrare de vita.* No butterfly ever turned back or circled again to the glade with its yellow cassia blooms where he had spent his caterpillarhood. Nor did he fly toward the North Star or the sunset, but between the two. Twelve years before, as I passed up the Essequibo and the Cuyuni, I had noticed hundreds of yellow butterflies, each true to his little compass variation of NNW.

There are times and places in Guiana where emigrating butterflies turn to the north or the south, sometimes for days at a time; but sooner or later the eddies straighten out, their little flotillas cease tacking, and all swing again NNW.

Today the last of the migration stragglers of the year — perhaps the fiftieth great-grandsons of those others — held true to the catopsilian lodestone.

My masculine pronouns are intentional, for of the thousands and tens of thousands of migrants all, as far as I know, were males. Catch a dozen yellows in a jungle glade and the sexes may be equal. But the irresistible maelstrom impels only the males. Whence they come or why they go is as utterly unknown to us as why the females are immune.

Once, from the deck of a steamer far off the Guiana coast, I saw hosts of these same great saffron wings flying well above the water, headed for the open sea. Behind them were sheltering fronds, nectar, soft winds, mates; before were corroding salt, rising waves, lowering clouds, a storm imminent. Their course was NNW, they sailed under sealed orders, their port was Death.

Out over the great expanse of the Mazaruni, the fluttering insects were usually rather evenly distributed, each with a few yards of clear space about it, but very rarely — I have seen it only twice — a new force became operative. Not only were the little volant beings siphoned up in untold numbers from their normal life of sleeping, feeding, dancing about their mates, but they were blindly poured into an invisible artery, down which they flowed in close association, almost touching, forming a bending ribbon winding its way seaward, with here and there a temporary fraying out of eddying wings. It seemed like a wayward cloud, still stained with last night's sunset yellow, which had set out on its own path over rivers and jungles to join the sea mists beyond the uttermost trees.

Such a swarm seemed imbued with an impulse of travel which surpassed discomfort. Deep cloud shadows might settle down, but only dimmed the painted wings; under raindrops the ribbon sagged, the insects flying closer to the water. On the other hand, the scattered hosts of the more ordinary migrations, while they turned neither to the north nor to the west, yet fled at the advent of clouds and rain, seeking shelter under the nearest foliage. So much loitering was permitted, but with the coming of the sun again they must desert the pleasant feel of velvet leaves, the rain-washed odors of streaming blossoms, and set their antennae unquestioningly upon the strange last turn of their wheel of life.

What crime of ancestors are they expiating? In some forgotten caterpillardom was an act committed so terrible that it can never be atoned for, except through the working out of karma upon millions of butterflies? Or does there linger in the innumerable little ganglion minds a memory of long-lost Atlantis, so compelling to masculine *Catopsilias* that the supreme effort of their lives is an attempt to envisage it? "All utter rubbish," says our conscious entomological sense, and we agree and sweep them aside. And then, quite as readily, more reasonable scientific theories fall asunder and we are left at last alone with the butterflies, a vast ignorance, and a great unfulfilled desire to know what it all means.

On this October day the migration of the year had ceased. To my coarse senses the sunlight was of equal intensity, the breeze unchanged, the whole aspect the same — and yet something as intangible as thought, as impelling as gravitation, had ceased to operate. The tension once slackened, the butterflies took up their more usual lives. But what could I know of the meaning of normal in the life of a butterfly — I who boasted a miserable single pair of eyes and no greater number of legs, whose shoulders supported only shoulder blades, and whose youth was barren of caterpillarian memories!

As I have said, migration was at an end, yet here I had stumbled upon a Bay of Butterflies. No matter whether one's interest in life lay chiefly with ornithology, arrowheads, politics, botany, or finance, in this bay one's thoughts would be sure to be concentrated on butterflies. And no less interesting than the butterflies were their immediate surroundings. The day before, I had sat close by on a low boulder at the head of the tiny bay, with not a butterfly in sight. It occurred to me that my ancestor, *Eryops,* would have been perfectly at home, for in front of me were clumps of strange carboniferous rushes, lacking leaves and grace, and sedges such as might be fashioned in an attempt to make plants out of green straw. Here and there an ancient jointed stem was in blossom, a pinnacle of white filaments, and hour after hour there came little brown trigonid visitors, stingless bees whose nests were veritable museums of flower extracts — tubs of honey, hampers of pollen, barrels of ambrosia, hoarded in castles of wax. *Scirpus* sedge or orchid, all were the same to them.

All odor evaded me until I had recourse to my usual olfactory crutch, placing the flower in a vial in the sunlight. Delicate indeed was the fragrance which did not yield itself to a few minutes of this distillation. As I removed the cork, there gently arose the scent of thyme, and of rose petals long pressed between the leaves of old, old books — a scent memorable of days ancient to us, which in past lives of sedges would count but a moment. In an instant it passed, drowned in the following smell of bruised stem. But I had surprised the odor of this age-old growth, as evanescent as the faint sound of the breeze sifting through the cluster of leafless stalks. I felt certain that *Eryops*, although living among horse rushes and ancient sedges, never smelled or listened to them, and a glow of satisfaction came over me at the thought that perhaps I represented an advance on this funny old forebear of mine; but then I thought of the little bees, drawn from afar by the scent, and I returned to my usual sense of human futility, which is always dominant in the presence of insect activities.

I leaned back, crowding into a crevice of rock, and strove to realize more deeply the kinship of these fine earth neighbors. Bone of my bone indeed they were, but their quiet dignity, their calmness in storm and sun, their poise, their disregard of all small, petty things, whether of mechanics, whether chemical or emotional — these were attributes to which I could only aspire, being the prerogatives of superiors.

These rocks, in particular, seemed of the very essence of earth. Three elements fought over them. The sand and soil from which they lifted their splendid heads sifted down, or was washed up, in vain effort to cover them. More subtly, dead tree trunks fell upon them, returned to earth, and strove to encloak them. For six hours at a time the water claimed them, enveloping them slowly in a mantle of quicksilver, or surging over with rough waves. Algal spores took hold, desmids and diatoms swam in and settled down, little fish wandered in and out of the crevices, while large ones nosed at the entrances.

Then Mother Earth turned slowly onward; the moon, reaching down, beckoned with invisible fingers, and the air again entered this no man's land. Breezes whispered where a few moments before ripples had lapped; with the sun as ally, the last remaining pool vanished and there began the hours of aerial dominion. The most envied character of our lesser brethren is their faith. No matter how many hundreds of thousands of tides had ebbed and flowed, yet today every pinch of life which was blown or walked or fell or flew to the rocks during their brief respite from the waves accepted the good dry surface without question.

Seeds and berries fell, and rolled into hollows rich in mulcted earth; parachutes, buoyed in thistle silk, sailed from distant jungle plants; every swirl of breeze brought spores of lichens and moss, and even the retreating water unwittingly aided, having transported hither and dropped a cargo of living things, from tiniest plant to seeds of mightiest mora. Though in the few allotted hours these might not sprout, but only quicken in their heart, yet blue-winged wasps made their faith more manifest, and worked with feverish haste to gather pellets of clay and fashion cells. I once saw even the beginning of storage — a green spider, which an hour later was swallowed by a passing fish instead of nourishing an infant wasp.

Spiders raised their meshes where shrimps had skipped, and flies hummed and were caught by singing jungle vireos where armored catfish had passed an hour or two before.

So the elements struggled and the creatures of each strove to fulfill their destiny, and for a little time the rocks and I wondered at it together.

In this little arena, floored with sand, dotted with rushes, and balconied with boulders, many hundreds of butterflies were gathered. There were five species, all of the genus *Phoebis*, but only three were easily distinguishable in life: the smaller, lemon yellow *statira*, the larger, orange *argante*, and the *philea*. There was also *eubele*, the migrant, keeping rather to itself.

I took some pictures, then crept closer; more pictures and a nearer approach. Then suddenly all rose, and I felt as if I had shattered a wonderful painting. But the sand was a lodestone and drew them down. I slipped within a yard, squatted, and mentally became one of them. Silently, by dozens and scores, they flew around me, and soon they eclipsed the sand. They were so closely packed that their outstretched legs touched. There were two large patches, and a smaller area outlined by no boundary that I could detect. Yet when these were occupied, the last comers alighted on top of the wings of their comrades, who resented neither the disturbance nor the weight. Two layers of butterflies crammed into small areas of sand in the midst of more sand, bounded by walls of empty air — this was a strange thing.

A little later, when I enthusiastically reported it to a professional lepidopterist, he brushed it aside. "A common occurrence the world over, *Rhopalocera* gathered in damp places to drink." I, too, had observed apparently similar phenomena along icy streams in Sikkim, and around muddy buffalo wallows in steaming Malay jungles. And I can recall, many years ago, leaning far out of a New England buggy to watch clouds of little sulphurs flutter up from puddles beneath the creaking wheels.

The very fact that butterflies chose to drink in company is of intense interest. But in the Bay of Butterflies they were not drinking, not during the several days when I watched them. One of the chosen patches of sand was close to the tide when I first saw them, and damp enough to appease the thirst of any butterfly. The other two were upon sand parched by hours of direct tropical sun, and here the two layers were massed.

The insects alighted, facing in any direction, but veered at once, heading upbreeze. Along the riverside of markets of tropical cities I have seen fleets of fishing boats crowded close together, their gay sails drying, while great ebony Neptunes brought ashore baskets of angelfish. This came to mind as I watched my flotillas of butterflies.

I leaned forward until my face was hardly a foot from the outliers, and these I learned to know as individuals. One sulphur had lost a bit of hind wing, and three times he flew away and returned to the same spot. Like most cripples he was unamiable, and resented a close approach, pushing at the trespasser with a foreleg in a most unbutterflylike way. Although I watched closely, I did not see a single tongue uncoiled for drinking. Only when a dense group became uneasy and pushed one another about were the tongue springs slightly loosened. Even the nervous antennae were quiet after the insects had settled. They seemed to have achieved a rhopaloceral nirvana, content to rest motionless until caught up in the temporary whirlwinds of restlessness which now and then possessed them.

They came from all directions, swirling over the rocks, twisting through nearby brambles, and settling without a moment's hesitation. It was as though they had all been here many times before, a rendezvous which brooked not an instant's delay. From time to time some mass spirit troubled them, and as one butterfly the whole company took to wing. Close as they were when resting, they fairly buffeted one another in mid-air. Their wings, striking one another and my camera and face, made a strange little rustling — crisp and crackling whispers of sounds — as if a pile of northern autumn leaves, fallen to earth, suddenly remembered days of greenness and humming bees, and strove to raise themselves again to the bare branches overhead.

Down came the butterflies again, brushing against my clothes and eyes and hands. All that I captured later were males, and most were fresh and newly emerged, with a scattering of dimmed wings, frayed at edges, who flew more slowly, with less vigor. Finally the lower patch was washed out by the rising tide, but not until the water actually reached them did the insects leave. I could trace with accuracy the exact reach of the last ripple to roll over the flat sand by the contour of the remaining outermost rank of insects.

On and on came the water, and soon I was forced to move, and the hundreds of butterflies in front of me. When the last one had left, I went away, returning two hours later. It was then that I witnessed the most significant happening in the Bay of Butterflies — one which shook to the bottom the theory of my lepidopterist friend, together with my thoughtless use of the word "normal." More than two feet of restless brown water covered the sand patches and rocked the scouring rushes. A few feet farther up the little bay the remaining sand was still exposed. Here were damp sand, sand dotted with rushes, and sand dry and white in the sun. About a hundred butterflies were in sight, some continually leaving, and others arriving. Individuals still dashed into sight and swooped downward. But not one attempted to alight on the exposed sand. There was fine, dry sand, warm to a butterfly's feet, or wet sand soaked with draughts of good Mazaruni water. But they passed this unheeding, and circled and fluttered in two swarms, as low as they dared, close to the surface of the water, exactly over the two patches of sand which had so drawn and held them or their brethren two hours before. Whatever the ultimate satisfaction may have been, the attraction was something transcending humidity, aridity, or immediate possibility of attainment. It was a definite cosmic point, a geographical focus, which to my eyes and understanding was unreasonable, unsuitable, and inexplicable.

As I watched the restless water and the butterflies striving to find a way down through it to the only desired patches of sand in the world, there arose a fine, thin humming, seeping up through the very waves, and I knew the singing catfish were following the tide shoreward. And as I considered my vast ignorance of what it all meant, of how little I could ever convey of the significance of the happenings in the Bay of Butterflies, I felt that it would have been far better for all of my green ink to have trickled down through the grains of sand.

CHAPTER 21

St. Francis of the Plaster Cast

IN my journal I find under date of May 14 that it is a red-letter day because we are at last moving up for good to Rancho Grande. On the following day the few paragraphs are rather less coherent, descriptive of a peculiar combination of a sloth, of Pedro, and of a ladder (which I strove to hold aloft) falling on me and by some miracle breaking only my leg. It confirmed the old saying that the only time it is unlucky to walk under a ladder is when you are carrying it.

It was the first time for many years that my osseous system had been interfered with. I was forthwith bundled down to the *clínica* at Maracay, a hospital efficiently modern and comfortable. I was X-rayed by my friend the president of the Rotary Club, and swiftly plaster-casted by two jolly, joking surgeons. It was not until four weeks later that one of the jokes appeared to be on me, because nothing had been put between my skin and the cool plaster. When it came time for me to emerge from my cocoon, I realized how slightly I had departed (in at least one character) from those stout fellows, my hairy Cro-Magnon forebears.

Next morning when my pleasant Venezuelan nurse came in, I smilingly told her to her horror that I had been bothered all night by the humming of vultures. She was quieted later when it turned out that I had confused the Spanish words *zamuros* and *zancudos*, and that I had been attacked by nothing more grisly than mosquitoes.

I was back at my laboratory table in twenty hours, but for some time interests were divided. The most depressing phase in my new life was the dread of becoming a dope fiend in the effort to secure sufficient sleep. The jeers of my companions as to the ability of ten grains of aspirin to unlock a future of frightfulness were unconvincing. I recall in my dreams holding up my hands to see if they were yellow and shaking, and looking in the glass to detect the pin points to which my pupils were reduced. All the horror tales I had ever read were explicit on the pin points!

A day came when with the aid of a pair of crutches it was possible to lever the cast and myself into the air and forward, and hobble out on the great stone veranda. I sat down on the upper step and thought about my work. To think about what a naturalist wishes, or ought, to do to justify himself in the opinion of the world, or, what is much more important, in his own estimation, is exceedingly easy: merely a matter of observation, analysis, and synthesis. Actually to accomplish this is something else again.

The unknown and unexpected enters frequently into this sort of jungle research, and two small adventures, one physical and one mental, were, at this moment, rushing toward me out of the future. I hitched down two steps, then another two. Impatience at this tripodal locomotion seized me, and I tried four steps at once.

Many years ago I won a medal for the same method of propulsion in an athletic contest where the activity was pole vaulting. There was a difference, however. In the latter exercise one ran with exceeding rapidity, holding in his hands a long pole, toward a crossbar suspended at a height which, to the approaching contestant, looked stratospheric. At the propitious moment the end of the pole was thrust against the ground; one trusted one's weight to it and by sheer impetus rose high into the air.

By a fortunate concatenation of swinging up body and legs, flattening out at the zenith, letting go of the pole at a precise instant, one cleared the bar, hurled the pole back into space, and dropped with a thud into a soft bed of sawdust thoughtfully provided by the field attendants. Then one rose to one's feet, dirty but triumphant, provided the pole had fallen back and the crossbar still remained undisturbed. By this complicated chain of events a human being has been able to push himself skywards off the face of the earth a distance of more than fifteen and a half feet.

The attempt to take four descending steps at once turned what might have passed as a new style of pole vault into a horizontal distance event, and very nearly sent me back to the Maracay *clínica* with a second broken bone. My amateur status in the use of double crutches and a single leg lifted my body into what must have been a creditable aerial curve, and landed me across the drive into a soft bed of daisies. This resulted in a stinging jar to the cast leg, but wrought no damage to the good one.

This minor experience would have passed quickly from mind were it not for what followed. I and my crutches were assembled in a camp chair, and with the game limb in another I settled down for that rarity at Rancho Grande, a sun bath. I planned for an hour or two of only casual watching of the wild creatures in sight, but a very curious thing happened.

Years ago, in the *Atlantic Monthly* I read an article called "Twenty Minutes of Reality." As I remember, it had to do with a sudden, brief, inexplicable clarity of mental vision. Drinkwater did a somewhat similar thing in "A White Night."

A few minutes after I settled down in the chair, there came to and through my mind a vivid sense of the interrelationships, the synthesis of all that one's eyes saw. I had the feeling that if this could be sustained for even a brief time, many scientific problems would be cleared up. The sensation came and passed so rapidly and unexpectedly that the conscious residue was extremely small. If realization of the uniqueness of the occurrence could have been accomplished by relaxed reception, much more might have remained in memory.

One sequence alone made me realize that the entire experience was very real, more than a cerebral turnover, a self-hypnotic *as if*. The most active ingredient in my visual environment in front of the entrance to Rancho Grande was the flock of violet and white swallows, fly-catching in mid-air. To my sudden clarity of perception the birds ceased to be individuals, each hawking on its own, each beginning and ending where my eye encountered and left it. It took its place as part of an unending sequence, whose beginning was back among life's beginnings, and whose end was far in the future. I saw a single bird as a segment, a bit of an arc from a complete circle, which my eye had picked up and would leave in a few seconds.

My particular bird caught a small butterfly without any disturbance of its smooth curve of flight; it swept up to a hole in the masonry of the great castle, thrust the insect into the gaping mouth of a hungry young one, swung back into flight with a neat white packet of excrement. This dropped into a clump of bushes and vanished from view, but my mind never lost sight of it. The bag of lime burst, and the ingredients spread and sank and at once began to fertilize whatever root they splashed. The vegetation, the leaves, gained strength and shot up, and the eggs of the mate of the devoured insect (or another, no matter) hatched upon it, and the larva fed and gained strength to pupate and take to wing as another butterfly for another swallow, and so circle without end. (In whispered parenthetical conceit I recall that Alfred Whitehead in a refinement of stimulating philosophy once said that "if you have had your attention directed to the novelties in thought in your own lifetime, you will have observed that almost all really new ideas have a certain aspect of foolishness when they are first produced.")

I finally mastered the technique of those excellent homemade crutches and demanded a chance to do jungle work. I was motored two hundred yards to the summit of Portachuelo Pass and thence became a most awkward quadruped and crutched my way through tall grass, which recalled swimming through dense sargassum weed. My goal was a small flat terrace, exactly in the center of the pass, from which I looked down the most tropical of gorges, up at the cloud jungle of Pico Periquito, and around at a dense undergrowth of melastomes, palms, and tree ferns. Only at an unforgettable place called Ghoom, en route to Kinchenjunga in the Himalayas, between Nepal and Sikkim, have I seen moss and air plants equal, in luxuriance and abundance, to those of this pass.

With a leg, which seemed no longer a part of me, propped up on a low, cut bough, and seated in a rookha chair bought forty years ago at Whiteaway-Laidlaw in Calcutta, I was as content as a crocked-up human can be. I looked around with little hope of doing more than amuse myself with some sentimental twaddle for the eyes of my journal alone; some mouthings on the lives of the small folk whose abode had been crashed. I imagined some such sweet maudlinity as "Watching the Wildings," or, "Cute Doings of My Jungle Friends."

The spate of life which accepted me as an utterly harmless prop was quite unexpected. This ranged from the peering vulture who licked his chops (or would have, if he could lick and had chops), happily hoping that my accident would get steadily worse, to the optimistic spider which spread his net between cast and chair. Doves to St. Francis, vultures to me. He loved his, I fooled mine.

Every day when the swirling *neblina* held back, banked in the distant valley fronting on the sea, I spent a few hours in my roost, sitting, looking, and writing. My journal notes are all fragmentary, records of small events, approaching, arriving, and passing as they do in life anywhere. In many cases I planned to pursue some observations to a logical conclusion when by the happy interference of serendipity my attention was sidetracked, my intention switched to a new aspect of tropical life. So my St. Francis days were casual, relaxed, and, to myself, wholly delightful.

June 4.   8 A.M. to Noon:

On this day in the heart of the jungle, almost three fourths of a mile above the sea, seated between the arms of my chair, and it in turn cradled in the hollow between two mountain peaks — I felt as if I were really sitting on top of the world. This first cripple-jungle-day was wonderfully clear and warm. A few wisps of the fog hung against the distant western peak, but soon dissolved.

In struggling through the tangle of tall grass, I found that the present season was the peak of the harvest for beggar-lice, and clothing, socks, and cast were covered. These seeds were the only inconveniences of the day, real emigrants from everywhere, wholly alien to this tropical world. The first probably fell from one of the rare passing trucks, perhaps a stowaway from New York itself. Europe, Asia, Africa, any cleared roadside area is home for them.

In an interval of the impact of living things I plucked a stick-tight from my garb and looked at it through a hand lens. This is fatal to any further satisfaction derived from unaided vision, and into a vial went the grappling seed for later home study. Only when I reached my table did I realize what a wholly needless concern such precaution was in the case of these superhitchhikers.

The air is heavy with perfume. Beside and under my chair is a tropically beautiful junglet of variegated leaves and floral spires of blue and purple, beloved of insects. For a time we planned to use these colorful plants as background for paintings of various jungle animals, and then we discovered that they were the common, or garden, *Coleus*, pompolluda, or Jacob's-coat. Here, far from their original home, the small flowers tremble under the eager feet of Venezuelan flies and bees. Coleus has made itself at home much more pleasantly for me than the sticktights.

Scattered among these plants there is growing in abundance a curious rib-leaved, starched affair, springing directly from the ground and a foot or two in height. It bears the very human name of *Carludovica*, belonging to a strange family squeezed between the palms and arums. It is really a stemless palm, appropriately known as palmilla, and also answering to the pleasant mouthful of jipijapa. It is closely related to the species which is the source of our Panama hats. These, in turn, appear to be thus called because they are made in the hinterland of Ecuador.

I sit in the shade of a high shrub, a melastome, whose sprawling branches arch overhead covered with masses of eight-petaled, pinkish-white flowers, with hairy, sticky buds and stems. This family is one of the few tropical ones which I can recognize from the curious longitudinal veins of the leaves, curving from base to tip. I break off a cluster and find the blossoms very lovely, both in color and in the graceful arrangement of their inflorescence. A stout, flat-topped pistil leans up and forward, while twelve stamens, six on each side, bend far back and then up, and their elongate anthers turn forward again, the whole suggesting the appearance of a Japanese flower arrangement representing a breaking wave. The scent of these blooms is strong and very pleasant to me and to the host of insects which fills the air with a continuous underhum. So much for the plants within reach.

I shut my eyes for a moment and thereby shift my ears into high gear. There comes a faint whirr after whirr, and overhead I see occasional swallows — the blue-and-whites — as they swoop uphill and pass within arm's reach. Their usual flight is swift and erratic, and, near their nests in our old Rancho Grande building, is unpredictable. But here in the midst of their daily hunt for insects they keep to regular beats over and between certain trees. I count one swallow eight and another seven times, both wing-molt-branded, passing over a curved air route, one between two small branches and the other just above. Twice they come at the same time. The return is made out of sight but regularly, for in a very short space of time they again appear swooping uphill.

A blue tanager flies to a cecropia, hangs upside down beneath the great leaves and finds three luscious caterpillars. The bird eats one and carries the others to a palm frond, pounds them into tenderness and gulps them down. Wiping his bill clean, he looks up and listens. So do I, for a spine-crinkling sound rises and falls in the distance — the overture of a chorus of howling monkeys. While I am straining to hear, a butterfly flits past, and after it is out of sight, my subconscious sight, adulterated for the moment by concentrated listening, comes to the surface with a rush: even Edward Everett Horton could not achieve a more perfect double-take. The chorus dies in my eardrums and I realize that I have seen, not a butterfly, but one of the loveliest of day-flying moths — *Urania* — most rare at this elevation, thirty-six hundred feet. Only near sea level occur those wonderful migrations of tens of thousands of these insects, so exquisite in their blacks, whites, iridescent greens and blues.

The tanager and I glance up and with varied emotions watch another bird fly past. To me it is only a female blue with beakful of caterpillars, headed for her nest in the top of a neighboring palm. To the first bird it is his own mate. A human husband caught in such a situation would rush about, grab the first food available and smugly follow swiftly in the wake of his unselfish spouse. Tanagers have their own ideas, and while my azure gourmand follows his mate, he is empty-beaked. In nest building, incubation, and brood feeding I have found much variation in individual birds, but I never recall anything which in coarse anthropomorphic language I could call dereliction of duty.

The butterflies alone, which come swiftly or falteringly up the steep pathway of the gorge trail below me, could occupy every moment of eye and mind to tell adequately of their flight, the cause of their dalliance, their advertisement of their stealth, their senses, their search. My favorites are slow-flying; flutteringly proclaiming their inedibility. They are *Heliconius melpomene*, although why these fearless, confident, lazily contented butterflies should be humanly tagged with the name of the Muse of Tragedy was for long sheer mystery, and the reason for it, whatever it may be, can in no way compare with the unknown cause for their pattern of twin scarlet bosses on the field sable of their aerial shields. Their name, however, proved to be quite as reasonable as my tongue-in-cheek interpretation of their deliberate flight as "fearless, confident, lazily contented."

Common as these butterflies were to prove, they always seemed to possess a hint of Noah's Ark animals and went through life two by two or even one by one. Only once did I experience a real Melpomene day, when, in this very spot, I counted sixty-eight, all brand-newly emerged, shining and beautiful, come slowly up the gorge. They were dallying even more than usual. There was a strong wind over the crest and when they suddenly struck it, they either gave way and were blown back down again, or they dropped into the underbrush, sought out a protected leaf and waited patiently for better weather. The sun came out later, and the wind slackened or else went higher into the sky, and they all began to feed on every blossom in sight. Never before had I seen them thus, probing eagerly with their long spiral tongues. They were unbutterflylike in their reaction to one another, perhaps an incipient courtship. A sipping butterfly would suddenly be butted and buffeted by a flying companion. The least touch on my part or that of any other creature would have sent the feeding insect off in fear, but in these cases no attention was paid, except to cling to the blossom the more tightly. However, this rough, head-butting affection resulted in nothing.

I caught two, handled them and let them go, and the net, my fingers, and the whole air of the glade was filled with the strong odor of witch hazel. When thus disturbed, the abdomen curved around, two of the segments parted slightly and there appeared a pair of yellow protuberances, which moved in and out. The odor was cleanly and pleasing to my senses, but it apparently is a potent defense, as all my gang of tasters later refused to have anything to do with Melpomene.

Postscript:

Six months after the above was written I sat in my library in New York still wondering about the significance of Melpomene's name. I opened the yellow-edged pages of my precious copy of Linnaeus's

Systema Naturae for 1758, the Bible, the Domesday Book for all taxonomists.

I found that on page 458 where the author began playing nomenclatural Adam to butterflies, he discarded all descriptive names suggestive of color, pattern, texture, form, or locality, and systematically pre-empted what would correspond to a telephone directory of all the gods, goddesses, and socialites of Greek mythology. On the first two pages of his list we find butterflies baptized with the names Priamus, Hector, Paris, Helenus, Troilus, and Deiphobus. We know the species of insects thus designated, and although assigned by the illustrious Swedish naturalist one hundred and ninety-seven years ago, these names are still in general use. Any attempt at reconciling sex, character, achievements, personal attributes, nobility, or moral turpitude of these Grecians with the delicate, colorful butterflies bearing their names is quite futile. In considering the names as names for a while, light emerges, the mystery is solved, for there is no mystery. We realize that Linnaeus's mind systematically dissected a Grecian Burke's *Peerage*, for in these names (including Polytes, Number 7, on the following page) we have King Priam of Troy and his six sons. Perhaps some sense of delicacy on the part of the author made him reserve for still another page Numbers 18 and 19, Helen and Menelaus.

With this suggestive discovery as a lead we turn to pages 466 and 467 and find in order the names of all nine Muses, from Terpsichore to the ninth and last, Melpomene. This is not all. Linnaeus recognized one hundred and ninety-two species of butterflies as known to him in 1758, and he naïvely grouped them all under the term or genus *Papilio*, which would have identified these insects to any Greek schoolboy. But from here on mythology holds sway and we find Priam and his sons heading the group, band, or phalanx (or subgenus) of Equites Trojani, or Knights of Troy. Melpomene, in turn, is one of fifteen species including Apollo and the sacred Nine which are appropriately assembled under *Heliconii*. Helicon was, as we know, the Mount or meeting place of Apollo and the Muses. Thus we enjoy discovering that Linnaeus is as neat, exact, and logical in his mythological as in his biological classifications.

The name of Melpomene once solved, my continued curiosity as to all other early published references to the butterfly *melpomene* steadily snow-balled.

Linnaeus in a single sentence of eleven Latin words precisely and accurately describes *melpomene*: "Oblong wings wholly black, basally red below: fore wings with a red band on both sides." I hoped for some pertinent and amusing comment such as the author makes upon the domestic cat: "When roused is most agile; makes love wretchedly, with yowling and squabbling." But concerning *melpomene* there is only, "Habitat in America."

There is a list of four references which Linnaeus collated as mentioning this butterfly. The first is "George Edwards (T. 38)."

The second reference is a series of barren abbreviations: "Sloan. jam. 2. p. 219. t. 239. f. 25, 26." This refers to Hans Sloane's *Natural History of Jamaica*, two large, fascinating volumes, replete with copper plates, which appeared in London in 1725. Fortunately, I possess a copy and find an unmistakable *melpomene* described on page 219, and pictured on plate 239. But this appeared in pre-Linnaean days when binomials were still in the future. It is exactly as if a letter addressed to myself would read The-tall-lanky-bald-headed-New-York-naturalist-who-likes-to-study-jungle-creatures, instead of William Beebe. So instead of the Linnaean and our modern custom of referring to the present butterfly as *Heliconius melpomene*, Hans Sloane is compelled to recite The-black-Darien-Butterfly-with-two-spots, or more technically *Papilio-Cartagenius-nigrescens-alba-linea-prope-extremitatibus-alarum!* Thank God for

Linnaeus and brevity. The black and white engraving is good and an improvement on many recent illustrations in that the wings are figured relaxed in a much more natural position than when strained far forward in the conventional entomological fashion. Of casual notes we are only told that " 'tis common . . . and was sent from Cartagena."

From the Latin description we learn that the wings are brown with white transverse bands, so we can be certain that Hans's specimen was sadly faded by the sun for a long time. It was perhaps exposed for the entire twenty years' delay in the appearance of this second volume. These two decades become understandable when we read a charming sentence in the Introduction: that the first volume "begot a very earnest Solicitation from many People, for whom I have a very great Regard, to publish this Second which hath been delay'd chiefly by a multiplicity of Business in the Practice of Physick, which I esteem one of my first Cares, and must be minded, if the Lives of Persons be regarded, with due Attention to the several Symptoms and Changes of their Diseases." I know of no better excuse.

To return to the butterflies in the gorge. Another elegant floats past in shining steel blue with a quartet of white lines drawn firmly across the forewings; easy to look at, easier to describe, but humanly impossible to explain. The name of this blue and white beauty is more reasonable, *alba*.

What looks like our Gulf Fritillary, *Agraulis vanillae*, alights within a yard of my hand, revolves slowly, until oriented, flattens its wings, and becomes a sun worshiper here as elsewhere. It proves to be the identical species of our northern fields, with a slight color shift to a different subspecies.

Four parrakeets come streaking up the valley, two by two, the

family bond always apparent even at the height of speed, the pairs
being distinguishable even at forty m.p.h. They veer low overhead
and suddenly seeing me sprawled out in the chair burst their alar
and vocal throttles wide open in increased velocity and frantic
screams. From the deep shades of the giant liana-hung trees below
me arise three bird songs, all sweet, all different, utterly unknown.
Then comes the silvery descending phrase of a long-legged *Gral-
laria*, the great ant-bird tenant of the deepest jungle dusk.

Out of a tenuous cloud high up in the bluest of blue Venezuelan
skies, drifts the equally cloudlike moon, a half moon. Even with
my glass there is no hint of solidity or craters. Only the too regular half curve distinguishes it from the drifting cloud which passes
over it. Soon the moon will "change," an utterly human optical
term based on sheer shadow illusion. Nevertheless, this evanescent
vision is often a warning that after two or three days this sun-
drenched eyrie of mine will fill to overflowing with driving, mois-
ture-soaked fog, solid *neblina* for the succeeding half week.

A fluttering bird goes over; another appears and blunders into a
bunch of leaves. Birds do not blunder like this, but a grasshopper
might and this is one of the giants of all grasshoppers. I watch
others come singly, or two and three together in sight at once, but
in no sense with a feeling of flock or swarm. Yet they show a faint
sense of sociability of sorts. First one, then two, then four flutter
up and cling to the trunk of the same cecropia; others alight on the
foliage above. In the space of ten minutes, four of the trunk climb-
ers creep slowly toward one another, until ten feet will include
them all. In my lens I can see the four feet walking slowly, the
great muscled hind legs raised somewhat off the surface, ready at
hair trigger for the pull of necessity to catapult the owner into
space, whence the wide scarlet wings resume their heavy efforts and
carry it, always to the south, toward the lowland hot plains; three

butterflies pass in as many minutes, none of which I have ever caught or seen in any collection.

Now occurs what turns out to be the high light of the morning. A head peers out from the leaves at one side of the rough branch in front of me. Lidless eyes do not move, but a forked tongue plays and vanishes. Without jerk or visible impulse the head moves toward me and there follows five feet of a beautifully patterned, brilliant boa constrictor. To freeze, on my part, requires no conscious intention. It is chiefly surprise at seeing the snake at this altitude. I had thought of boas always as tenants of low, hot-country jungle. The serpent wavers along the double branch which forms my top rest, stopping only when it reaches my cast, which rests on the same support. The head bends slightly and twice the tongue plays and replays against the plaster. Then without change in pace it flows on, coils for a moment on the farthest limb and pours its length slowly to the ground. For several yards, by the slight waving of the coleus spires, I can trace its course, and then it passes forever.

A minute black speck floats across my field of view; warning perhaps of disturbed vision, or a tiny fly walking across the lens of the instrument? Neither. Without moving the glass except to slip it sideways off the trunk, with my fingers on the focusing screen I twist sharply and, apparently as high up as the clouds if not indeed as the moon, a bird soars into clarity. Could it be the first condor in this range? No, decidedly it could not. The size of any bird of prey is difficult enough to judge when the bird is perched by itself in a tree, but when it is soaring at an indeterminate height with nothing but the moon for comparison, any guess is futile. Then luck was with me, and my bird banked slowly; then sharply it did an Immelmann turn and showed every side, top and bottom. Not a feature was absent, and I knew I was looking at an osprey. Anything familiar in this landscape leaves me astonished, and an osprey above Portachuelo seemed wholly alien. But there it was, and I wondered if it was one of the same birds I had watched a few months before over the waters of Long Island. In Venezuela all ospreys are like myself, temporary *émigrés*, citizens of North America.

Twenty minutes of quiet passed, then a loud humming arose from behind the chair and I froze. The sun was full out and the silhouette of my head rested on a canvas bag hung on the branch. On my hat in sharp outline was the ebony figure of a humming-bird. I sat motionless, heard a momentary buzz, and on the screen saw a change of position, a shift in pantomime. Then a cloud obliterated the little black shade and in the ensuing sunshine he had vanished, this time silent as a butterfly, or his own shadow. His feather planes are not only gravity defying, they can soften and muffle sound itself. His physical being was invisible, but I will never forget him. A glance at my hat showed a tiny speck of white, and I was flattered that the hummingbird had made himself at home.

I reached out and picked one of the slender, ribbed cyclanthid leaves; then looked beneath seven others. All but one were tenanted by bespangled little spiders, whose name *Gasteracantha* is as long as eight of them laid end to end. The anterior of their two corporeal divisions was jet black, with the pointed abdomen of a general amber. Upon this was etched an elaborate pattern, two elongate shoulder patches of black, looking like little wing covers. Further toward the tip of the body were two black spots. Between the patches two broad lines of bright yellow were drawn and below them three vertical bands of the same color. Finally, on the sides, glowed a pair of irregular yellow blotches, where the artist's brush had slipped. I list all this maze of pattern and color because it is on a body one sixth of an inch long, a body living on the underside of an overarching, low-growing leaf. A single glance upward of a lizard or bird would reveal the edible morsel, although in size it would rank more as a vitamin pill than a full course.

Four of the half dozen spiders were females, and each, when disturbed, rushed to a tiny silken sphere, dangling in mid-air beneath the leaf like a tethered inverted balloon. These swinging globes were only an eighth of an inch across, but very precious to their creators. Later, on my laboratory table, I carefully opened the outer layer of the circular swaddling clothes, and found spheres within spheres, thirty-seven perfect globes; and the smooth, shining, lustrous texture compelled the timeworn simile of pearls. Each was barely one fiftieth of an inch. No signs of development were visible, just the primordial homogeneous substance of seven and thirty potential spiderlings, swaying in the Portachuelo sun and fog, guarded by a minute harlequin parent. No tumultuous capture in a huge inexplicable glass vial, wielded by a creature so enormous that he must always be beyond the ken of the diminutive spider — none of all this terrible experience diverted her a moment from her arachnid devotion.

This under-leaf business could go on forever, but a last peek beneath an eighth leaf revealed no harlequin spider, but another species, mother and young, as utterly unlike as a gracious Whistler's-mother type would be with a low-life murderous offspring.

My eyes wandered idly a few feet down the gorge trail where several recently cut steps revealed an exposure of slimy yellow clay. All the good it had been to us was to make certain a quick, slithering descent and not on our feet. Other beings found the clay of real personal use, and at this moment a loud buzzing arose from a great, yellow-banded, hairy, bumbling bee who was packing the panniers on her thighs full to the brim with the malleable earth, housing material ready at hand. She rose as I watched, buzzed impatiently, re-alighted and scraped off a bit of supercargo. Again a brief helicopterlike lift into the air, again an angrier buzz, and down she came. This time she scraped at the left saddlebag, apparently having found herself off an even keel in flight. A third time she jettisoned a skim of clay, madder than ever about it, and now she gathered her legs beneath her, gained six-feet elevation, carefully flew in a circle and came slowly upgorge and over my head. She was logy, cargo laden down to the plimsoll mark, but satisfactorily answering her propellers, safe on her way. I never saw her again, but will never forget her so-human mental and physical interactions: patience, impatience, overambitiousness, anger, perfect physical balance, cautiousness, ultimate success. I know, you instinct purist; elide all these anthropomorphisms, as do I, but it's fun to think them, all the same!

I turned to look under a ninth leaf — but here I am ordered out of the chair; I hobble stiffly back along the track which seems a mile now, into the car and on to Rancho Grande.

Postscript:

In the course of freeing my clothes from their coat of vegetable pinfeathers I recalled my hand-lens glimpse of one of the seeds. In the laboratory I put one on the microscope stage. A simile almost ceases to be a simile when comparison with another object shows a difference of size alone. Such is the case with the beggar-lice seed and a three-pronged south-sea-island fish spear. The only difference except size would appear to be the ultimate object of each. The human-made spear transfixes a fish and then retains it, while my grappling seeds desire only a firm grip on some moving thing, animal or human, to hitchhike to a favorable place for growth. Their lack of discriminatory anchorage is only too evident from the hundreds lying under the laboratory chair after my effortful molting.

The Melanesian fisher assembles a trio of sawfish beaks or lashed shark's teeth or the spines from the tails of sting rays, and then fits this lethal trident into a short head. A bamboo or reed handle, perhaps six to twelve feet in length, and the weapon is ready. Look at such an instrument through the large end of a pair of binoculars, so that twelve feet appears to be reduced to one half inch, and you have the beggar-lice seed of Portachuelo.

The widespread trident (or occasionally bident) arises from a head about three times its length, and the base of this ends in a narrow ring. The ring appears to be hollow, and only the bamboo handle is lacking. This short head is delicately fluted with eight rounded, longitudinal bas-reliefs in all, worthy in perfection of supporting the plinth of a Parthenon. In color it is ebony.

Under a still higher power, the whole head is seen to be completely covered with a multitude of extremely minute spines, each stout and sharp as its profile shows. I count the number in a square millimeter and conservatively estimate them at fifty-six hundred and twenty-five. The columnar head is eight and a half millimeters in length, and this plus the circumference provides anchorage for a minimum of one hundred and forty-three thousand of these infinitesimal spines, all sharp, all pointed toward the prongs, each eager to do its one-hundred-and-forty-three-thousandth part in adhering to my tweed or linen or flannel — or me.

As we approach the base of the trident, a new type of spine appears, each by itself, with a large base and a slender curved outline. These sprout at intervals along the ridge of the eight fluted folds. When we reach the trident, all is changed, and under the lens, in perfect focus, only in size do the prongs and spines differ from those of the Samoan fisherman. Each prong of the trident is, in turn, tri-ridged, and down each ridge is a series of cunningly slanted, long needlelike spines, all directed backward, pointing opposite to those on the head.

I glance at six spears on my microscope stage and one attracts and holds my attention. Here all similes end; here something is happening which could never be contrived by human effort. The beggar-louse is coming to life. When it has waited and waited in vain for the longed-for touch of a passing body, the seed at last sprouts where it was born. Out of the hollow ring at the base of the head there creeps a living something. A fresh simile, most appropriate, comes to mind: a moray eel half out of its coral cave. Already eellike, the slender root or stem has coiled about a neighboring seed. Moraylike, its colors are sinister — dull amber, upon which are smeared veins and blotches of dusky scarlet.

Thus my beggar-lice are as they are to one another, as they must appear to such a being as an ant. When I look at the scores still left on my clothing, when I think of the astronomically uncountable masses waiting on their stalks, similes, comparisons, simple descriptions ever falter and cease. By the grace of cunningly devised lenses my eyes have lived for a time in an inhuman, a most marvelous world, and I return from a contemplation of a seed of the commonest weed with renewed interest in my universe of orchids, birds, and mountains.

We reread the words we have written about these trident sticktights and they suddenly become thin and empty, a few phrases subconsciously intended to catch and perhaps for a few minutes to hold the attention of a reader; perhaps an honest hope that they may be wholly divorced from any personality or effort on the part of the author, and convey some of the fun he got out of the experience of being made the common carrier of a thousand hopeful seeds. Yet after all we have arrived nowhere, have settled or explained nothing. We leave the beggar-lice where we found them.

We can fly high over the pass and look down in vain even for the two boundary mountains. We can give a twist to the fine adjustment of an oil-immersion lens, or watch the proxy shadows of infinitely small atomic movements in our seed, and we still observe only unintelligible sections of its structural existence. We still are only a child peeping through a knothole in a fence at something seen indistinctly, and not at all comprehended.

The only real thing seems the uncoiling stem of a new generation, preparing to confuse new generations of naturalists.

June 6. *8 to* 11:30 A.M.:

I settle down in the same place close to the gorge at the summit of Portachuelo Pass.

Just as the *neblina* makes visible every breeze and shift and small whirlwind of the otherwise invisible ether, so at this moment I am certain that the air before me is filled with myriad insects. They are wholly invisible both to my eyes and binoculars, but are revealed by twenty-six blue and white swallows hawking and diving or swooping up to a stop like the apogee of a lobbed tennis ball. On the single jungle telephone wire which stretches down and down the dark trail are perched sixteen young swallows, their exact juvenile age revealed by the less or greater extent of tail feathers, in addition to which all those with short, stubby tails have much more baby yellow at the gape. In the sunlight this bright color is as useless as a rainbow. Five days ago in the dim recesses of a nesting hole in the castle wall of Rancho Grande this spot of pigment made all the difference between meals and no meals. It played the part of an effective colored beacon in the semidarkness to guide the bug-filled beaks of the parents to their goal. Swallows cannot count, and an unfortunate nestling without this jaundiced reflection might well be passed by in favor of his two sisters with helio-graphic lips of saffron.

The present wire-perched wights with ridiculously abbreviated tails and excess of oral gamboge all, as in a trained chorus, raise their heads, open their beaks, and flutter their wings as first one, then another adult swallow swoops close. I see only a single flutter among the older young. To my scientific mind, it is a perfect ex-ample of the delicately graduated weakening of an instinct whose usefulness is passing.

In the case of the supplicating adolescents there was no distinc-tion in favor of rightful parents. Any moving bird meant merely a potential ration of gnats, a purveyor of flies. No parent, rightful or otherwise, paid the slightest attention until one weak-willed mother with an overdeveloped issue complex alighted near a yellow-faced infant and stuffed it. The effect of this delayed devotion spread rapidly and three adjacent young tried to sidle along the wire toward the free-lunch bar. But the feet of baby swallows are not made to sidle and two promptly fell off. Their wings were stubby, their tails negligible, yet the practiceless, untrained, inherited skill of innumerable generations of master fliers imbued every muscle, every sense, and both of the fledglings caught themselves in mid-air and, when perilously close to the tree ferns below, swung around and up and joined the maze of parents and neighbors.

I watch two swallows come together in the air, one adult, the other nearly grown. Their feet grip, clinging closely together, their wings vibrate, and although held almost vertically, they lose hardly any altitude. The beaks approach, meet, and one actually pushes within the other, jamming down a tangled mass of insects, all within a second's time, and as skillfully as if the young bird were gaping at the entrance of the nest. Once observed, this mid-air feeding proves to be a common occurrence, a little feathered duplication of an airplane carrier being refueled in mid-ocean. Mother and young drop from their momentary aerial suspension and melt into the flock. I watch the youngster and within a few seconds the malingering infant has pursued and caught two insects for himself.

The cloud of gnats moved to the north — I know this because the flock of swallows shifted in that direction, busy as ever, and soon not one bird was in sight. Thirteen of the remaining young followed, rather tremulously. On the long expanse of wire there was left a single lone bird — a tiny feathered Dopey, who sat and peered here and there, held fast by timidity, dumbness, bravery — who am I to infect it with my anthropomorphic suggestions? My attention wandered down the gorge, and toward me came on motionless wings a turkey vulture, hoping against hope to find me more nearly in the fit state "to set before a King" (vulture).

The baby swallow saw the vulture before I did and with a single sharp chirp fled on wings of fear, swiftly as its grandfather had ever done, toward the distant flock. Parent swallows perch on the barbed wire in the compound of Rancho Grande with never a second glance at the vultures soaring close overhead, but the present conditions were very different. The key of differentiation between harmless members of the *Falconiformes*, to wit *Carthartidae*, as opposed to the deadly *Accipitridae* had not been a required thesis in this young swallow's kindergarten semester. The youthful *Pygochelidon cyanoleuca* was taking no chances. His ancestral knowledge told him a bird of prey was a bird of prey, and he wisely decided not to wait to ascertain whether its dietary preferences tended toward living or defunct prey.

The vulture circled me once and then reluctantly left. I shall never know whether his abrupt discouragement was due to his discernment of my change in method of progession. For today I had graduated from my quadrupedal character of the two crutches of yesterday, toward the more nearly normal-human props of a single crutch and a cane. The vulture was a fellow living creature on our planet, perfectly adapted to his niche in life, living it normally, successfully, and as I watched his black form drift away in graceful, effortless flight, I felt for him nothing but sheer admiration and envy.

The whole flock of swallows swung back again over my gorge, and now they were joined by a numerous company of large, bi-planed dragonflies. For fifteen minutes there was a friendly inter-mingling of birds and insects, both absorbed in reducing the popu-lation of Portachuelo insects.

As I watched the flying birds and insects, I thought what a grand thing it would be if only the sky trails of volant beings would last for a time like prints in the dew or tracks in new fallen snow. Phy-sicists have their cloud chambers wherein atoms and their neutrons and protons register their paths in lines of light. How nice, like vapor skywriting, if birds could leave at least transitory trails be-hind them. Think of the sun rising after a night at the height of migration, and what an awe-inspiring sight the sky would present, with its thousands upon thousands of avian trails.

Now and then I was visited by one or another of my staff, visits solicitous or fortuitous. I would hear heavy running steps, pounding along the invisible road to my right, and the hearty swish of a net as Henry Fleming hurled himself after some ill-fated butterfly, probably as diminutive as it was rare. There would instantly follow an indistinct mumbling, wholly wordless, but perfectly indicative of satisfaction or a bitter disappointment. At this distance it sounded as must have the first, primitive vocal attempts of our apish ancestors, endeavoring to communicate emotions in the absence of words. Except for a matter of millions of years Tegumai might have been passing down the road toward Ocumare.

A rustle in the grass behind might indicate Jocelyn Crane, lugging her thirty pounds of movie camera and tripod, in search of Portachuelo creatures and happenings to imprison on innumerable frames of color-conscious film. Seldom was I able to share my high lights with my fellows. A full hour or two of solitary, vegetative, cabbagelike inactivity seemed necessary to induce the more intimate occurrences.

At ten o'clock Jocelyn again announced her presence behind my chair by a violently shaken bush, a local hurricane inspired by the hope of the fall into her inverted umbrella of some female salticid spider in a desired condition of "expectancy."

We both turned at the same moment and exclaimed, for in the air just overhead was something totally unexpected — the biggest beetle in the world, scientifically termed *Dynastes hercules*, in full flight in full sunshine. This event gained in importance, for it proved to be the only time we were ever to see this giant of all insects in daylight.

For the last few minutes of my stay, before I was called for, I was bent double in my chair. My last notebook page was used up and I had to scribble the remaining notes on the smooth surface of my plaster cast, later in the laboratory to be typed off. I might have written on my cuffs, but in the jungle we don't wear cuffs.

There came an interesting sequence to the young-swallow-on-a-wire episode at the pass as I looked out early the next morning from the laboratory windows. It was a day of *neblina* and the gray vapor swirled down from the pass, twisting and writhing like a crowd of unhappy spirits. If Homer had been standing beside me, he would have quoted his own words: "These airy shoals of visionary ghosts

... " So dense was the mist that a wire fence only thirty feet away was dimmed, while the nearest jungle trees were faint smudges in the drifting landscape. On the five strands of wire at irregular intervals, like notes of the staff of some slow-moving musical phrase, were eleven young swallows. Some were younger, some very slightly older. The Rancho Grande colony of blue-and-whites is the only one hereabouts for miles, so some, if not all, of yesterday's youngsters must be those of today, differing only in being a day older and perched on a fence instead of telephone wire.

What instantly attracted and held my attention was the fact that every swallow child was being persistently fed by one or both parents. I was able to make certain that at least in one case the same bird repeatedly fed the same fledgling. She had lost a left wing feather, not by molt, and time after time she returned to her particular offspring, who was perched on the second strand of wire, a g note in the little largo composition.

It seemed quite certain that the youngsters recognized their individual parents, for, unlike the day before, only one or two of the lot fluttered hopefully, hailing an approaching meal ticket, and these were invariably the ones fed. In most cases the beak of the provider bristled in every direction like the rictal feather-hairs of some outrageous flycatcher. These resolved into the sprawling legs of crane flies, which for an unlucky reason had chosen this inauspicious day to swarm.

The point of especial interest was that these same birds were being fed twenty-four hours after a corresponding period of intentional neglect. I watched and found out that as the driving mists dissolved and the sun began to fight through, and insects increased, the young birds, one by one, took to wing and hawked for themselves. This was checked on a succeeding clear sunrise, and on another *neblina* morning, and I realized that the recrudescence of the feeding was correlated with the difficulty of seeing and capturing food on the part of the immature amateur air pilots.

The method of feeding repaid watching. The usual routine was for the parent to hover in front of the fluttering, wide-gaping young, and by a forward impetus of the wings, hummingbirdlike in its assurance, to reach out and jam beak and insects down the infantile gullet. Frequently, however, the parent came up with a rush and alighted close to the young bird. In spite of frantic begging no effort to feed was made until the swallow rose in the air again, hovered, and fed from the wing. This was a distinct continuation of late-nesting feeding, when the youngsters, two or three in number, lined up at the edge of the nesting hollow, awaiting their moment of blissful gorging.

As the matutinal feeding frenzy slackened and the humidity came down to ninety-nine and nine tenths per cent, there began most elaborate, acrobatic toilets on the part of whole families on the wires. A tiny foot would be lifted over the wing to scratch the head; wing and tail were stretched to the utmost and preened assiduously. The oil gland was constantly tapped and the breast feathers fluffed and combed. The neck was finally stretched far out and down, and this, curiously enough, seemed to be the most difficult feat of all, for in two cases it resulted in complete loss of balance, with consequent instantaneous recovery.

I left my vantage as the first shafts of sunlight struck on the opposite jungle slopes, but before I went, in the space of a few minutes, the avian cycle turned full swing. Most of the young had flown, but a pair of old birds remained, and began an intensive courtship — intensive, that is, for swallows. On top f wire a male pirouetted in a perfectly dignified manner, flirting his wings and jerking his head from side to side. After these dances he made a wholly abortive attempt at mating.

The last swallow to swoop past carried a long pliable strand, adumbration of a new home, the last of the innumerable generations stretching back through so many centuries.

June 7.   Turiamo:

My cast and I were driven through the gate of Rancho Grande. Whenever I leave thus, with our retainers, Manuel, Pedro, and Eduardo, waving us out, I feel as if seated in an anachronistic prophecy of something separated by centuries from our medieval surroundings. Winding and twisting to the limit of road-making possibilities, we coast down through dense, drenched subtropical forest. The unbelievable extremes of our environment still continue, for here is the most smooth and well laid of modern concrete, and any minute, as has happened, we may sight in the road serpent, rare jungle bird, or even jaguar.

We roll lower and lower, leaving the cool, saturated tree ferns and air plants, into extreme dryness, until we move in the shade of acacias and sight tall, skyscraping cacti, like the serrated sky line of a city. Turning off the straightaway to Ocumare de las Costa, our little fishing village, we shift abruptly west and negotiate ruts and rocks and the moraines of last season's landslides, and finally wind down to sea level and skirt one of the loveliest of bays — Turiamo.

I sit in the shade of a coconut palm facing seaward toward the wide entrance of the bay, an entrance broken only by a tiny rocky cone of an islet off shore, topped with a toy chimney of a lighthouse. The mountains rise steeply on each side, covered with dense woods, and extending around the whole landward horizon. The glowing, golden araguanay trees which dotted the slopes six weeks ago are now gone, replaced by the white constellations of frangipani. In spite of its ubiquity in India, this temple flower is a real native of this country.

Along the shore to the left is a fringe of acacias, sea grape, and manzanilla trees, leaving a narrow, shelving, sandy beach. By the lowness of the upper line of jetsam we know how slight are the tides. Out from near the point on this side extends a discolored, narrow, fingerlike streak underwater, and my trio of scientists are at present happily wading about, gazing with nostalgic memories through the waterglass. Later they report a perfect reef, or *arrecife*, complete with dominant corals, alcyonarians, anemones, bryozoans, and inhabited by all the common reef fishes, brilliant demoiselles, parrots, and some which are new to their Bermuda-trained eyes.

At the inner curve of the bay, still to my left, are the first coco palms, and where I sit these expand inland into a far-reaching grove. They continue behind and on to my right in a straggling fringe to where there begin the equally straggling and far less beautiful houses and huts of the decimated village.

The wharf on the far side of the bay is hidden from me by the most dominant feature of the landscape — a great three-masted schooner some distance along the shore, with uplifted bowsprit overhanging the sand of the beach. The keel at the bow is well above the surface, and the rest of the wreck extends straight seaward at a downward angle of about thirty degrees. It foundered twelve years ago, and now the tangled rigging and the two remaining forward masts are useful only as perching places for martins and terns, while the half-submerged davits and railings far aft are pre-empted by solemn pelicans. I see rough-winged swallows going in and out of the hawser holes, and even without visual proof I can assume the schools of brilliant fish milling around in the shadow sanctuary of the great ship.

The palms are heavy with clusters of nuts, and each of them leans far over, as lean they must, toward the sea. Upon its proximity, for some unknown reason, their very existence depends, but too great emphasis upon this juxtaposition often results in tragedy and death. To the left a cluster of eight palms rises high toward the sky, each careening like a vegetable Pisa, only much more gracefully. Between them and the beach is another equally tall tree full of fruit whose flotsam natal nut a century ago sprouted too near high tide. Some recent storm had cut into the three-foot bank, crumbled it, and left the tree with only the slightest support for the mass of Medusa roots which forms the underground part of this stately plant. Already the seaward slant of the trunk is perilously acute and the tips of the longest fronds sway and nod as the waves reach up and brush them. Half the roots have lost all grip upon the sand, and the crisis will come along before the crop of nuts is ripe. Nothing but block and tackle could save it now, and what to improvident human beings is one coco palm more or less!

When it falls, it will lie across the body of a former neighbor, a palm with its rooted head far out in the surf and its trunk upcurved in an arch over the sand as if in a dying effort to recover its balance. Closer to me, a still older root mass projects from the waves, like the long spines of some gigantic urchin. And so along the shore lie the bodies of other palms which grew slowly through the years of long ago, forever watching the fateful approach of the merciless sea. In ages past all this level foreshore was deposited by the same breakers. Now it seems as if in obedience to the whim of some cruel god of the sea, the waves begin to take back what they gave.

Over the tops of the lofty mountains at my back there creeps a soft, fleecy grayness, the first hint of the *neblina*, the clouds which leave the heavens, descend upon the upper jungles and change their name to fog. This tenuous mist now assumes a darker, more sinister appearance, and when I look again, half of the mountain horizon is oxidized by vertical lines of hathi gray. At the exact moment of noon a drop of water falls on my paper and partly obliterates a split infinitive. Another and another and another, and I hastily cover my binoculars and pad, and curl my ankle with its plaster cast beneath me. I am not quite ready to have it dissolved.

I crouch far over in the old instinctive attempt to keep my stomach dry, only then remembering that until it too shares the drenching, I shall be most uncomfortable. Flannel shirt and khaki trousers change color and cling closely; drops palisade from my hat brim; the fronds which so kindly shaded me a few minutes ago now turn to elegant fountains, each a spillway, an emerald spout. For once in my life I cannot run for shelter to an adjacent deserted shed, so after the first discomfort and instinctive revulsion at losing my comfortable dryness I settle down and enjoy the sound on the dead fronds, the spattering on the salty sea, the various degrees of translucency of the air.

The last drop falls, my friends arrive from the reef, and we all start back, I learning a wholly new crutch technique in the soft sand and then being carried bodily by my husky entomologist over a foaming inlet. The unique feeling of being transported by a fellow human being, of sensitive suspension and acute consciousness of every step, took me back to the Himalayas when three Tibetans, with the aid of two stout poles, once ferried me, a third of a century back in time, across a swift, rock-riven, icy stream born of the glaciers high above on the upper slopes of Kinchinjunga.

We sit damply in the car and eat our lunch, and with the first hint of the sun I look back and count two hundred and forty-eight martins crowding two long strands of slack and sloping rigging on the old wreck.

On the way back we stopped in front of a ramshackle thatched house, with a group of Turiamians leaning back on cowhide-seated chairs, reminiscent of the country store and cracker barrel. Four men, with perfect pirate make-ups, were playing dominoes with grains of corn for chips. I asked if the maize stood for money, and they gave me a shocked chorus of, "*Oh, no, no, señor!*"

Beyond the village a wide salt-dried flat drew our attention, and I crutched about, happily kicking over the sign of vanished kine. The manure was old and dry, but it sheltered scarabs, giant ants, several kinds of crabs, and glistening jewels of tiger beetles. These latter, instead of taking swiftly to wing, scurried into the nearest crab holes. All I had to do was to invert a glass jar over the hole and rest patiently on my crutches. Before long, up would come the beetle in frantic haste with a crab in swift pursuit. While I was resting in the blazing heat to mop my forehead, my eye caught a line of interested spectators along the high bank of the road. They were wholly absorbed in us, and I longed to be near enough to hear their comment on these insane *Norteamericanos* who seemed to derive pleasure from the concentrated inspection of bovine guano, while the female of the species was lying flat on the clay with hand and arm deep down a crab hole!

Our good car labors back through the sand, holding the passing interest of a pair of black-necked stilts in a lagoon. Then we climb steadily out of the cactus and acacias into orchid-laden tropical growths, on through the scent of frangipani to where a jacamar appears, first inhabitant of this second altitudinal zone. One backward glance shows the sun slanting over the green palms, which, from here, look like the little paint-smelling growths balanced on wooden stands which used to come out of childhood's Noah's Ark.